Proceedings
of the
Twenty-Second Annual
BIOLOGY COLLOQUIUM

THE BIOLOGY COLLOQUIUM

THE annual Biology Colloquium at Oregon State University, in a spirit of informal discussion, provides opportunity for participation from the floor and for personal contact with visiting scientists over a two-day period. Initiated in 1939 by the Oregon State Chapter of Phi Kappa Phi, the Colloquium receives the support, assistance, and collaboration of various organizations including Sigma Xi, Phi Sigma, and Omicron Nu and the departments of Oregon State University concerned with biology. Grateful acknowledgment is made to the National Science Foundation for its support, to the biologists and other scientists who have contributed to the programs, and to the officials of the University and the State System of Higher Education for encouragement and assistance.

The theme, date, and leader of the Colloquia have been as follows:

Recent Advances in Biological Science, March 4, 1939. DR. CHARLES ATWOOD KOFOID of the University of California.

Ecology, March 9, 1940. DR. HOMER LEROY SHANTZ, Chief of Division of Wildlife Management, U. S. Forest Service.

Growth and Metabolism, March 8, 1941. DR. CORNELIS BERNARDUS VAN NIEL of the Hopkins Marine Station, Stanford University, in collaboration with DR. HENRIK DAM of the University of Copenhagen.

The Biologist in a World at War, March 14, 1942. DR. WILLIAM BRODBECK HERNS of the University of California.

*Contributions of Biological Science to Victory, April 3, 1943. DR. AUGUST LEROY STRAND, biologist and president of Oregon State College.

*Genetics and the Integration of Biological Sciences, Apri 22, 1944. DR. GEORGE WELLS BEADLE of Stanford University.

Aquatic Biology, April 27, 1946. DR. ROBERT C. MILLER of the California Academy of Sciences.

Biogeography, April 19, 1947. DR. ERNST ANTEVS of the Carnegie Institution of Washington.

*Nutrition, April 10, 1948. DR. ROBERT R. WILLIAMS of the Williams-Waterman Foundation.

*Radioisotopes in Biology, April 23, 1949. DR. EUGENE M. K. GEILING of the University of Chicago.

Viruses, April 29, 1950. DR. W. M. STANLEY of the University of California.

Effects of Atomic Radiations, April 21, 1951. DR. CURT STERN of the University of California.

*Conservation, April 19, 1952. DR. STANLEY A. CAIN of the University of Michigan.

*Antibiotics, April 18, 1953. DR. WAYNE W. UMBREIT of the Merck Institute for Therapeutic Research.

*Cellular Biology, May 6, 1954. DR. DANIEL MAZIA of the University of California.

Biological Systematics, April 30, 1955. DR. ERNST MAYR of the Museum of Comparative Zoology, Harvard University.

Proteins, April 6-7, 1956. DR. HENRY BORSOOK of the California Institute of Technology.

Arctic Biology, April 19-20, 1957. DR. IRA LOREN WIGGINS of the Museum of Natural History, Stanford University.

*Photobiology, April 11-12, 1958. DR. F. W. WENT of the California Institute of Technology.

Marine Biology, April 3-4, 1959. DR. DIXY LEE RAY of the University of Washington.

*Microbial Genetics, April 22-23, 1960. DR. AARON NOVICK of the University of Oregon.

*Physiology of Reproduction, April 14-15, 1961. DR. FREDERICK L. HISAW of Harvard University.

Insect Physiology, April 27, 28, 1962. DR. DIETRICH BODENSTEIN of the University of Virginia.

Space Biology, April 12-13, 1963. DR. ALLAN H. BROWN of the University of Minnesota.

Proceedings available from Oregon State University Press.

Physiology of
Reproduction

FREDERICK LEE HISAW, SR.
Colloquium Leader

Physiology
of
Reproduction

Edited by

Frederick L. Hisaw, Jr.

Proceedings of the
Twenty-Second Annual
Biology Colloquium
April 14-15, 1961

OREGON STATE UNIVERSITY PRESS

Corvallis, Oregon

*Cover illustration drawn by Rafael Rodriguez and reproduced
by permission of Arthur T. Brice*

COLLOQUIUM PARTICIPANTS

Speakers, Presiding Officers, and Committees

Colloquium Leader:

FREDERICK LEE HISAW, SR., Fisher Professor of Natural History, Harvard University, Cambridge, Massachusetts.

Colloquium Speakers:

EMANUEL M. BICKOFF, United States Department of Agriculture, Agricultural Research Service, Western Utilization Research and Development Division, Albany, California.

PERRY T. CUPPS, Professor of Animal Husbandry, University of California, Davis.

WILLIAM S. HOAR, Professor of Zoology and Fisheries, University of British Columbia, Vancouver.

ANTON LANG, Professor of Biology, California Institute of Technology, Pasadena.

LEONARD MACHLIS, Professor of Botany, University of California, Berkeley.

Presiding Officers:

IRA S. ALLISON, Professor of Geology, Oregon State University; President-elect of Phi Kappa Phi.

RALPH BOGART, Professor Dairy and Animal Husbandry, Oregon State University.

FREDERICK L. HISAW JR., Assistant Professor of Zoology, Oregon State University.

JAMES E. OLDFIELD, Professor of Dairy and Animal Husbandry, Oregon State University; President of Sigma Xi.

HARRY K. PHINNEY, Associate Professor of Botany, Oregon State University.

Colloquium Committee:

FREDERICK L. HISAW, JR. (chairman), RALPH BOGART, VERNON H. CHELDELIN, F. A. GILFILLAN, H. P. HANSEN, HUGH F. JEFFREY, JR., JAMES D. MOHLER, J. KENNETH MUNFORD, JAMES E. OLDFIELD, AUSTIN W. PRITCHARD, SZU H. WU.

Phi Kappa Phi Executive Committee:

GLENN A. BAKKUM (president), IRA S. ALLISON (president elect), WILLIAM E. CALDWELL (past president), HENRY TEN PAS (secretary-treasurer), J. KENNETH MUNFORD (journal correspondent).

Sigma Xi Executive Committee:

JAMES E. OLDFIELD (president), CLARA A. STORVICK (vice president), ROGER G. PETERSEN (secretary), GEORGE S. KOCH, JR. (treasurer).

Phi Sigma Executive Committee:

LEE PURKERSON (president), GLENN STEWART (vice president), RUTH MARSHALL (secretary), BILL BROWN (treasurer), JUDY MILLER (editor), WILLIAM BRANDT (faculty adviser).

Omicron Nu Executive Committee:

JUDITH Y. JOHNSON (president), JUDITH COLEMAN (vice president), SALLY MYERS (treasurer), CONSTANCE MEYER (secretary), PATRICIA GUILEY (editor), Mrs. VERA WELLS (faculty adviser).

Dairy Club Executive Committee:

MIKE SEPPA (president), JOHN IRVING (vice president), DON CLAYES (secretary), KEN MESSERELE (treasurer).

Food and Dairy Technology Club Executive Committee:

E. A. DAY (adviser).

158270

Opening of the 1961 Colloquium

DR. A. L. STRAND
President of Oregon State University

ON FRIDAY, April 14, 1961, at 1:30 p.m., the Twenty-second Annual Biology colloquium was opened by Dr. F. L. Hisaw, Jr., Chairman, as follows:

Ladies and gentlemen, at this time I would like to call on Dr. Strand to open the Twenty-second Annual Biology Colloquium. Dr. Strand, as you know of course, is President of Oregon State University, and I now turn this session over to him.

DR. STRAND: Dr. Hisaw, Dr. Hisaw, Sr., our other speakers from British Columbia and California, and all participants in the Twenty-second Annual Biology Colloquium: For a number of years now I have been invited to make some opening remarks at these annual convocations about biological matters, and I know that is because of my position rather than any claimed or alleged qualifications as a biologist, which I am afraid I have long since left behind. Usually what I have to say is indicated on the program as "Greetings," but I was surprised this morning when I came to the campus and glanced at the Daily Barometer to see in rather large type that I was scheduled to give the opening address at this meeting. But I have been nonplused over things I saw in the Barometer before, and so I knew I had better look closer, and, sure enough, the reporter or editor, whoever wrote it, was a poor observer. This is the trouble with students; their observations are often careless. If he had looked at the program closely, he would have found that my address had been shortened by the Committee by the dropping of one 'd', so it appears as "adress," and I don't need to have a house fall on me to take a hint, so I know the Committee doesn't wish me to make any address.

Libraries and dens, attics and basements, and a lot of places are filled with what MacLeish termed the "paper rubbish" of our lives, and very often some of us try to write something that just adds to the rubbish, and little else. A lot of things have already been published so much better than I, or most other people, can write that unless we can really add something original, the effort, I think, is a poor investment.

Now, as an introduction to the Biology Colloquium, or indeed I would say to almost any scientific meeting, there is a perfect statement, or as near perfect as I can imagine anything to be, in the March number of *The American Scientist*, by Warren Weaver of the Alfred P. Sloan Foundation. The title is "Imperfection in Science." It is really a supplement to C. P. Snow's little book on the two cultures, and certainly it is a splendid statement as an interpretation of the philosophy of science at the present time. If you haven't read it already, I would recommend it to you earnestly. It fits just at this time. I wish Dr. Weaver were here to give it again, but anybody can read it.

I am very pleased to have a chance, and I think this is my last one, to recommend our leader from Harvard. I think it is a nice coincident that the chairman of our Colloquium Committee could invite his father to serve as the leader of this Colloquium. We are very glad to have him and the other speakers from British Columbia and California with us on the campus. I think we owe a special debt to the institutions in California, the University and the California Institute of Technology, for the contributions and speakers they have made available during a good many years in the past, so I welcome you to these meetings.

Theoretically the people in the audience have a right to break in any time they wish and ask questions, and are invited to make nominations from the floor after the Committee on Nominations has reported. It is seldom done, but a conversation ought to be a two-way proposition. One of the objects of the colloquium is to interest people who are not biologists and to at least clarify some things that are under discussion here so that nonbiologists who are interested will have some understanding of what is going on. So I am pleased to welcome you to this Twenty-second Biology Colloquium. Thank you.

Contents

The Evolution of Endocrine Adaptations of the Ovarian Follicle*

FREDERICK L. HISAW
The Biological Laboratories
Harvard University

I AM VERY grateful for the invitation to take part in your 1961 colloquium and am happy to be here during your most beautiful season of the year. This is appreciated especially by one who has been trying to endure the discomforts of an unusually severe winter. Also, your program committee should be highly commended for choosing the time of year most appropriate for discussing the physiology of reproduction in animals and plants.

Reproduction is one of the cardinal attributes of all living things and although the end result in all instances is the same, the ways by which it is accomplished may be quite different. In fact, the process of reproduction has acquired so many diverse, adaptive specializations in the course of organic evolution that only brief mention of those that are known probably would require more time than is available for our discussions. Consequently, only a comparatively few aspects of the physiology of reproduction can be considered, and necessarily will include mostly problems whose solutions have

been the research concern of the speakers.

However, there are common "red threads" that run through the general pattern of thought on most problems in this area of biology and unify the subject as a whole. Also, the purposes of a colloquium are served best when they include not only presentations of factual information but also theoretical considerations and new problems with conjectures as to their solution and probable significance. Therefore, it is with this attitude that I undertake a discussion of certain features of ovarian physiology.

The chief function of an ovary is of course the production of ova, and although, with few exceptions, little is known about the physiology of egg formation, there are considerable morphological data that suggest functional relationships. These include a number of specializations that take place in the ovum and associated tissues during the development of an oöcyte which are of special interest to an endocrinologist. Among these are such things as the relation of nurse cells and follicle cells to the oöcyte, the storage of yolk, how and from where it is obtained, and the materials utilized in its formation.

* Aided in part by N.S.F. grant 11213 and U.S.P.H.S. grant A-2673.

1

It seems that one of the first evolutionary problems that an ovum encountered was that of providing an adequate source of energy for embryological development during the interim between fertilization and the issuance of a viable individual. Under the most primitive situation it seems probable that the ovum may have been capable of accumulating sufficient yolk through its own metabolic efforts but apparently very early vitellogenesis exceeded the capacities of a single cell.

For instance, among colonial organisms, as in volvox, macrogametes or eggs apparently grow and store yolk with the assistance of other members of the colony with which they are connected by intercommunicating protoplasmic bridges. In Porifera and certain Coelenterata, such as hydra, the ova obtain their food stores by engulfing or fusing with smaller neighboring interstitial cells; and instances of association with special trophocytes also occur (Hyman, 1940). The manner of acquiring yolk by the ovum has received either scant or no consideration in most investigations of reproductive processes in animals; so arrangements similar to those mentioned may be more common than it seems.

A unique innovation is found in the Platyhelmenthes and seems to have arisen within the Turbellaria (Hyman, 1951). Here it is found that the yolk supplies of the egg are usually not stored in the oöcyte but in special cells, the yolk or vitelline cells, which are considered to be altered oöcytes. Also, in Lecithoepitheliata (Hyman, 1951) some of the oöcytes become eggs and others form follicle cells which surround each egg and pass food materials into it. Therefore, such ovaries have a proximal germinal area in which oöcytes are produced, and as the follicles are organized and grow they are arranged in a linear series of increasing size toward the oviduct (Figure 1). In others, as is most Turbellaria, there is a complete separation of the germinal area of the ovary from the yolk-producing region which is modified into

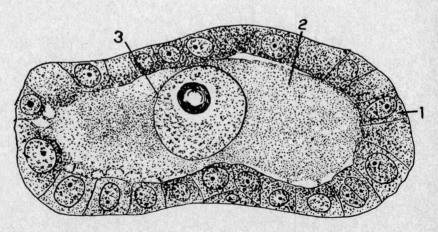

Figure 1.   A follicle of the germovitellarium of *Prorhynchus*, showing maturing ovum surrounded by a follicle of nurse cells, presumed to be altered ova. 1) follicle; 2) egg; and 3) nucleus of egg. (Hyman, 1951.)

yolk-glands or vitellaria. These ovarian specializations superficially resemble those of certain insects, although in most respects they are quite different.

Ovarian morphology and vitellogenesis in insects seems to be better understood than for most invertebrates (Bonhag, 1958; Telfer, 1961). The typical insect ovary is composed of a number of tubular (or more or less filamentous) parts, each called an ovariol, in which oögenesis and growth of the ovum occur. What seems to be the least specialized condition is found in the panoistic ovaries of older orders of insects such as Thysanura, Orthoptera, Isoptera, Odonata, and Plecoptera.

Fleas seem to be an exception and are unique in this respect among holometabulous insects. The ovariols of the more primitive insects (Bonhag, 1958) are thin-walled tubules with the germinal area next to the terminal filament and as the oöcytes pass down the tubule they increase in size and become surrounded by follicle cells. A feature of particular interest is the absence of nurse cells (Figures 2 and 3).

The oöcytes of most of the higher insects, in addition to being surrounded by follicle cells, are provided with nurse cells or trophocytes, which are considered as being modified oöcytes. Telotropic ovaries characteristic of Hemiptera and many Coleoptera have ovariols provided with a common trophic chamber with which the growing oöcytes maintain a connection by means of a nutritive cord (Figures 4 and 5) (Bonhag, 1958). Most holometabolous orders contain insects with polytrophic ovarioles in which the oöcytes have one or more trophocytes

which remain in close association with the oöcyte throughout growth and vitellogenesis (Bonhag, 1958).

Similar examples of the formation of ova could be cited for other invertebrates; but probably this should suffice to support the thought that oöcytes became self-insufficient for growth and vitellogenesis (if indeed they ever possessed it) quite early in evolutionary development, and consequently must rely in part, if not entirely, on other cells in the performance of such functions. That the ovum is capable of conducting extensive synthesis seems subject to question. Indications are that most of the constituents of stored yolk in a mature ovum were synthesized elsewhere and contributed in one way or another to the egg. Therefore, it is of interest to know something about what is stored and from whence it came.

Morphological evidence strongly indicates that a number of substances of several sorts are contributed to the yolk of ova by the nurse cells or trophocytes and surrounding follicle cells. In insects, these have been found to include sudanophilic lipids of a nonphospholipid type, phospholipids, RNA and DNA derivitives, and other less well identified materials. Telfer (1961) has shown by fluorescent antibody staining that in Saturniid moths proteins in the blood reach the surface of the oöcyte by passing between the follicle cells and are stored entirely in the yolk spheres. Although this process appears highly selective in that certain so called female proteins are preferred, foreign proteins such as a carotenoid protein and bovine serum albumin, when injected into the blood of a pupa during vitellogenesis, also enter

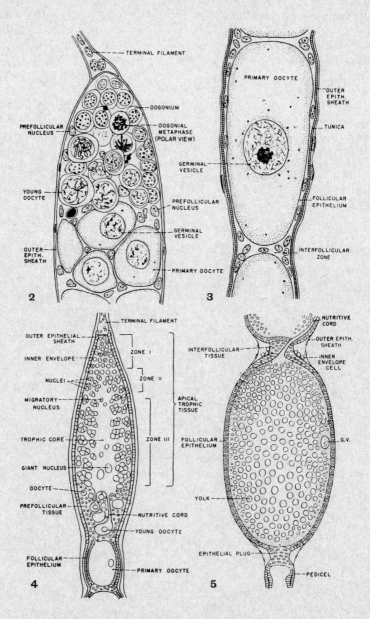

Figure 2.   Sagittal section of the anterior end of an ovariole of *Thermobia domestica* (Bonhag, 1958).

Figure 3.   Sagittal section of a follicle from an ovariole of *Thermobia domestica* (Bonhag, 1958).

the oöcyte to a lesser extent and are found unmodified in the yolk spheres (Telfer, 1960). Thus, it seems highly probable that components of the yolk in insects are derived from the blood, nurse cells (meroistic ovariols), and follicle cells.

There is extensive literature on the formation of yolk in the oöcytes of vertebrate animals and the observations and conclusions, for the most part, are in striking agreement with those for the invertebrates. The accumulation of serum proteins in the ovum of the chicken (Flickinger and Rounds, 1956; Knight and Schechtman, 1954) and of the frog (Cooper, 1948; Glass, 1959) and the passage of heterologous proteins from the circulation of laying hens to the ovum have been reported. However, it has not been established that in vertebrates, protein entering the ovum is stored exclusively in the yolk spheres as seems true of insects, but this difference may be due only to technical discrepancies. Therefore, the evidence at hand seems sufficient to warrant the conclusion that oöcytes obtain proteins directly from their environment and store them in the yolk (probably in the yolk spheres) without chemical modification.

There are, however, other aspects of vitellogenesis that are less well understood. One of these is the way by which substances from the blood and follicle cells traverse the cell membrane

of the oöcyte and thus gain entrance into the ovum. The best supposition that is in agreement with known facts is that this is accomplished by a process of pinocytosis (Telfer, 1961). The oöcyte surfaces of both invertebrates and vertebrates commonly have brushy projections or microvilli, structures that occur generally where rapid absorption is underway (Brambell, 1926; Chopra, 1960; Kemp, 1956). Also yolk spheres appear first at the periphery of the cell and, as the oöcyte grows and yolk accumulates, increase in size toward the center of the ovum. It also is assumed that growth of the yolk spheres results from fusion of the smaller ones near the surface of the oöcyte. Evidence for this is furnished by the observations of Yamomoto (1957) on vitellogenesis in the flounder, *Liopsetta obscura.*

Although there is much that supports the opinion that follicle cells contribute to the yolk, experimental evidence as to its nature is still wanting. Many observations based on light microscopy report extensions from the follicle cells which pass across the zona pellucida and make contact with or enter the oöcyte. Recent electron microscopic studies have shown this not to be true, at least in those animals that have been examined. Although there are extensions from the follicle cells which meet and intermingle with the microvilli of the oöcyte in the zona pellucida, and though contact is made,

---

Figure 4.   Diagram of a sagittal section of the anterior end of an adult ovariole of *Oncopeltus fasciatus* (Bonhag, 1958).

Figure 5.   Sagittal section of a follicle of *Oncopeltus fasciatus;* the oöcyte has not attained full size and the chorion has not yet been formed. G. V., germinal vesicle. (Bonhag, 1958.)

they do not fuse (Figure 6), so no direct protoplasmic connection between the follicle cells and oöcyte is formed.

However, there are indications of secretion by the follicle cells and probable absorption of the product by the oöcyte. The prolongations of the follicle cells contain material resembling that in the zona pellucida and configurations seen in the surface of the oöcyte indicate pinocytotic activity (Odor, 1960; Sotelo and Porter, 1959; Trujillo-Cenóz and Sotelo, 1959).

So, the ovarian function of oögenesis is associated with certain morphological specializations which are strikingly similar, if not identical, in both invertebrate and vertebrate animals. Such specializations obviously arose as facilities for vitellogenesis, which in its simplest form (though doubtful) may have been accomplished by the oöcyte without assistance. Yet, it is of interest that oöcytes having microvillar surfaces have been reported for several invertebrates as well as vertebrates, indicating they are at least of common if not uniform occurrence, and suggesting that all ova are capable of both rapid absorption and pinocytosis. Although this probably is true and also that as a rule oöcytes have more or less direct access to body fluids, they very early in ovarian evolution, as we have seen, became associated with trophocytes and follicle cells whose products were also contributed to the ovum.

Trophocytes, however, are not always present, even among related animals in which they occur, for instance in insects that have panoistic ovarioles, and consequently seem less important in the evolution of developmental processes. The trophic cells most commonly present in the organization of the invertebrate ovary are the follicle cells, which, on the basis of their morphological relation to the oöcyte, may be considered at least to this extent, homologous with the follicle cells or granulosa of the vertebrate ovarian follicle.

It also seems quite probable that such follicular adaptations in the invertebrate ovary involving maternal tissue may have constituted the morphological apparatus first utilized in the development of endocrine functions of the follicle. However, it may be helpful, for the sake of clarity, to digress briefly from this trend of thought and mention the hormones secreted by the ovaries of vertebrate animals.

The principal steroid hormones secreted by the mammalian ovary are estrogens and progesterone and the estrogens are primarily estradiol-17β and estrone. Much is known about the metabolic pathway for the formation of these hormones and it is now thought that the order in broad terms is cholesterol$\rightarrow$ progesterone$\rightarrow$ androgens$\rightarrow$estradiol-$17\beta\rightleftarrows$estrone$\rightarrow$ estriol. Estriol is a hormone found primarily in primates.

It also is of interest to know the distribution of these steroid compounds in the phylogenetic series and thus gain some idea of their association with the evolution of reproductive processes. There are quite a large number of reports of estrogenic activity in a variety of extracts of the gonads of widely different species but little is known regarding the chemical identity of the estrogenic agents in animals other than mammals. However, a few recent analyses have been made in which modern techniques for the iden-

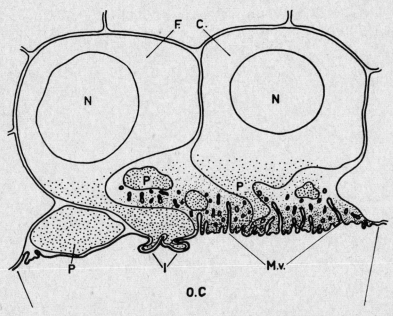

Figure 6. Drawing representing the border of an immature oöcyte from the rabbit with two follicle cells (F. C.). The space created by the separation of follicle cells from the oöcyte (O. E.) is occupied by ovular microville (M. V.). The amorphous substance of the zona pellueida is represented by stippling in the inter-cellular space. The portions of the follicle cells, prolongations (P), in which similar material is seen in the electron micrographs, are stippled somewhat more coarsely. Most of the prolongations are still wide at this stage and membrane interdigitation such as the one indicated at 1 are found over all portions of the oöcyte surface. N, nucleus. (Trujillo-Cenóz and Sotelo, 1959.)

tification of steroid compounds were used. Estradiol-17β, estrone, and estriol have been reported as present in ovarian tissues of the domestic hen (Layne, et al., 1958) and the lung fish, *Protopterus annectens* (Dean and Jones, 1959), and estradiol-17β, estrone, and progesterone have been obtained from the ovaries of the spiny dogfish, *Squalus suckleyi,* Wotiz, et al., 1958, 1960), salmon, *Oncorhyncus nerka* (Botticelli, et al., unpublished), and the ratfish, *Hydrolagus colliei* (Botticelli, et al., unpublished).

In the invertebrates, estradiol-17β and progesterone were isolated from ripe ovaries of the starfish, *Pisaster ochraceous* (Botticelli, et al., 1960), the sea-urchin, *Strongylocentrotus franciscanus,* and pecten, *Pecten hericius,* from which estrone also was obtained (Botticelli, et al., 1961).

The presence of these steroids in such distantly related animals indicates that they must have a very wide distribution. Also, it seems that most if not all of the more common steroids that function as ovarian hormones in the vertebrates have been in the organic world for a long time—indeed longer in geologic time than the vertebrates themselves. However, at what point in the evolutionary series such steroids assumed hormonal status is yet quite obscure. Although they also are present in certain invertebrate animals, no function is known for them. It is likely they may even be in plants. Estriol has been obtained from willow catkins (Skarzynski, 1933, 1934) and estrone from palm kernel extract (Butenandt and Jacobi, 1933).

Compounds having a cyclopentano-perhydro-phenanthrene nucleus characteristic of all steroid hormones are quite common in the plant kingdom. For example, *Dioscorea tokoro*, Makino, a Mexican wild yam of the Family Dioscoreaceae, contains diosgenin, a $\triangle^5$-sapogenin, which is used extensively as a starting material for the synthesis of progesterone and other steroid hormones containing the $\triangle^4$-3-keto group in the molecule (Heftmann and Mosettig, 1960). (Also, see Bickoff, page 93).

These observations suggest the possibility that the estrogenic steroids found in animals may have had their origin in plants. Yet, even if this be so, we are left to wonder how hormonal function of such compounds came about in animals. There is almost no direct information on this point, nor have the botanists discovered hormonal functions for such steroids in plants. It has been suggested informally that they may be simply components of oily food stores. This thought seems plausible and may apply equally to lower animals.

However, all estrogenic compounds, whether nonsteroidal substances derived from plants, or steroid hormones of animals or synthetic estrogens, have in common the ability to promote tissue growth by stimulating mitotic activity.

Bullough (1955) calls attention to this in his excellent review in which he develops the thesis that estrogens stimulate mitosis through their effects on basic enzyme systems such as those influencing glycolysis and the tricarboxylic acid cycle, which are essentially the same in animals and plants, including yeast and some bacteria. He theorizes that, "if then the basic biochemical systems are so similar throughout the animal and plant kingdoms, may it not be proper to speculate whether the basic factors, and in particular the hormones, controlling these systems are similar too?" This line of reasoning leads to the thought that promotion of growth by mitosis might have been the primary function of estrogenic compounds in both plants and animals and, as Bullough (1955) suggests, that in the vertebrates the relation of ovarian steroids to sex could have arisen as a secondary adaptation.

If this be so, then it seems possible that the estrogenic steroids in the ovaries of invertebrates may have little or no relation to sex. However, their growth-promoting action may be of importance for both follicular development and vitellogenesis, and probably also, as a component of the yolk, may stimulate growth during embryonic development. It is known that estrogens can stimulate mitosis in the granulosa of the ovarian follicle in vertebrates, but whether or not this applies to invertebrates is unknown.

The evidence we have considered seems to support the conclusion that in general the substances stored in the ovum are not the products of local synthesis within the ovum but were derived elsewhere and were obtained by absorption or pinocytosis. Proteins of the body fluid reach the surface of the ovum through channels between the follicle cells and are taken up by a highly selective process and stored probably entirely in the yolk spheres (Telfer, 1961). The nature of the substances contributed to the yolk by the follicle cells is less clear, but circumstantial histochemical evidence indicates that some are lipoidal (Bonhag, 1955, 1958).

Also, the prolongations of the follicle cells contain material resembling that in the pellucida (Trujillo-Cenóz and Sotelo, 1959), and it is assumed these products are taken up by the ovum. Furthermore, it has been observed that the protein-containing yolk spheres and lipoidal yolk bodies arise independently (Payne, 1932; Yamamoto, 1957; Bonhag, 1955) and that no cytoplasmic organelles in the oöcyte take a visible role in their formation (Payne, 1932).

If it be true that the follicle cells produce lipid as indicated, it seems a reasonable assumption that steroids, such as estrogens, also could be a component part. This would imply, of course, that follicle cells synthesize and secrete estrogenic steroids or in some way obtain them from the surrounding body fluid and transmit them to the oöcyte. Circumstantial evidence seems to favor secretion in those species of invertebrates in which the oöcyte is provided with follicle cells and in vertebrates whose ova store yolk.

However, the granulosa of the growing graafian follicle of mammals contains extremely little if any lipoidal material. But, the graafian follicle of higher mammals is a specialized structure in which vitellogenesis does not

occur, and it is adapted for a condition of viviparity under which the developing embryo does not depend upon yolk. Also, it seems quite probable that the estrogen that is present in the follicular liquor of mammals may be secreted entirely by the theca interna, a structure that is lacking in the ovaries of invertebrates.

Therefore, a thought that seems worthy of entertaining is that the secretion of lipids by the follicle cells might have been an early adaptation in both invertebrates and vertebrates and was lost in mammals. It would be of interest to know if a similar thing occurred in other animal groups, such as insects, in which vitellogenesis is greatly reduced in viviperous species (Hagen, 1951).

When one projects his thoughts toward the possible origin of conditions as seen at the present time in the vertebrates, it is immediately apparent that a number of morphological and physiological aspects of the problem that must be considered are of common occurrence in the animal kingdom. The general features of oögenesis, activity of the follicle cells, and vitellogenesis in the invertebrates and vertebrates are quite comparable. Also, the steroids, estradiol-17β, estrone, and progesterone, among others, seem to be ubiquitous, and closely related substances are present even in plants. So, the basic components essential for ovarian function were established in the invertebrates, and the chief differences between these pre-existing conditions and those found in the vertebrates are the results of various morphological and physiological adaptations.

The most important innovation appearing in the vertebrates is the en-

docrine control of ovarian function by
the pituitary. Certain other adaptations are the development of the theca
interna of the ovarian follicle, formation of the Müllerian system for trans-
porting large ova and the incorporation
of the corpus luteum into the endocrine
system.

It is obvious that ovarian function,
and particularly ovulation, must be
synchronized with certain external
phenomena, such as the most favorable
conditions for fertilization and sur-
vival of young. This requires that the
ovary receive certain information regarding the external environment as
well as events taking place within the
body. Such mediation is brought about
by secretion of gonadotropins by the
pituitary, in large measure, in accordance with information received through
the central nervous system and trans-
mitted to the pituitary via the hypothalamus. At what point in Chordate
evolution this appeared is not known.
There is strong evidence that pituitary-
ovarian interactions are well established in the cyclostomes (Agnatha),
(Pickford and Atz, 1957; Dodd et al.,
1960). There is equally strong evidence that the ganglion-subneural
gland complex of Ascidians (thought
by some to have pituitary homologies)
does not possess such a function
(Hisaw, Jr., et al., 1962).

Therefore, it seems probable that
pituitary-gonadal interactions were established at an evolutionary stage between protochordates and cyclostomes.

A speculative thought that may not
be idle, regards the possibility that a
tendency in certain vertebrates to store
large amounts of yolk in their oöcytes,
and consequently produce fewer and
larger ova, might in some way have
influenced the trend of adaptive specializations of the female reproductive
tract. It is obvious that large ova raised
the problem of their escape from the
body. It is conceivable that under the
most primitive conditions, and small
ova, the Wolffian ducts could have been
utilized for this purpose or abdominal
pores might have afforded egress as in
present day cyclostomes.

However, regardless of these possibilities the problem of large ova was
solved by the appearance of the Müllerian system. This specialization could
have been a gradual one as indicated
by the formation of the Müllerian
ducts in some species by a process involving longtitudinal splitting of the
Wolffian ducts, which in the males of
all vertebrates are retained for the
transmission of spermatozoa. Also,
rudimentary abdominal pores, characteristic of cyclostomes, have been reported in certain elasmobranches which
possess functional Müllerian systems.

(Note: Attention should be called to
the fact that rudimentary Müllerian
ducts may also be present in adult
males and are invariably found in
developing male embryos. This only
emphasizes the genetic basis of adaptations. Genetic characters of this sort
that depend upon hormonal action for
their functional development usually
are not confined to one sex. Also, it
has been suggested by some that the
vertebrates arose from an hermaphro-
ditic stock.)

Associated with these developments
in vertebrates is the appearance of the
theca interna of the follicle as a new
endocrine structure. In mammals, this
is quite generally considered the chief
source of estrogen secretion in the
ovary. The theca interna, as it de-

veloped, may, in fact, have tended to replace the follicle cells as a source of estrogens, if indeed they were, in the invertebrates and lower vertebrates. This may account in part for the almost complete absence of lipoidal material in the granulosa of the mammalian follicle where the theca interna apparently attains its greatest specialization.

Regardless of the validity of this thought, it is nevertheless an interesting fact that the theca interna was developed in juxtaposition to the follicle cells. This morphological relationship and the emphasis placed on estrogen secretion lend support to a thought expressed earlier that estrogens in some way had an important influence on follicular growth and directly or indirectly on vitellogenesis. These effects at first may have been due to the ability of estrogenic substances, present in nature or synthesized by the organism, to promote general growth through stimulation of mitotic activity, and later may have become more specifically concerned with follicular physiology and a component of stored yolk.

However, the development of a theca interna as an endocrine tissue is also correlated with the acquisition of a high degree of responsiveness to estrogen by certain structures outside the ovary. This was apparently true of all organs of the female reproductive tract derived from the Müllerian ducts, even from their very inception. Finally, most of the anatomical structures peculiar to the female in the various species of vertebrates, including certain brain centers controlling sexual behavior, were "captured" by the ovary and constitute the rather heterogeneous collection of things and functions commonly referred to as female secondary sexual characteristics.

Thus it seems that in some such way (as the one described) the estrogenic substances in nature may first have had a rather nonspecific or vitamin-like relation to reproduction. Next, they were adopted for more specific function in follicular growth and instances of synthesis by the follical cells might have arisen quite early. If so, at this point an estrogen became a hormone whose activities were concerned primarily with processes occurring within the follicle, the most important of which at this stage was probably vitellogenesis.

In the vertebrates, the enormous enlargement of the ovum is associated with the appearance of the theca interna, probably at first as a supplementary source of estrogen in accordance with the development of the Müllerian system and other extra-ovarian structures that had acquired responsiveness to estrogen. This expanding importance of estrogen was probably made possible, in large measure, by a simultaneous development of pituitary-ovarian interactions as a coordinating mechanism for regulating follicular activity in accordance with phenomena occurring outside the ovary. It was in this or a similar way that estrogen attained the status of a hormone of the body and was admitted into the endocrine hierarchy as queen of the realm of sexual reproduction.

However, estrogenic function in mammals, where it has been studied most thoroughly, is performed by a family of interrelated estrogenic steroids in which some are metabolites of others, but even so, estradiol-17β

seems to be the principal hormone of the graafian follicle in mammals, and the same is apparently true of other vertebrates (Wotiz, et al., 1958) and may apply even to invertebrates (Botticelli, et al., 1960, 1961). In view of the many possibilities, one wonders what properties peculiar to estradiol-17β were responsible for its selection as a favored follicular estrogen. It may be, of course, that estradiol-17β is in some special way better suited than other estrogens for participation in certain basic enzyme systems responsible for tissue growth. Also, a thought worth considering is the fact that of the natural estrogens estradiol-17β is not only one of the most active, but

also can give rise to estrone and, especially in primates, to estriol.

These three estrogens may constitute a most favorable combination for uterine development as the nature of their effects is somewhat different. Although this and other aspects of the problem are obscure, it is most significant that the principal estrogens in the vertebrates may have arisen in plants, remained in the invertebrates without obvious relation to sexual function, and attained definite hormonal status in vertebrates where they became involved in numerous morphological and psycho-sexual adaptations that appear basically the same in all species from fish to mammals.

Questions and Answers

QUESTION: Have extracts been prepared from the subneural glands for testing on immature or hypophysectomized mice or rats?

ANSWER: Several different investigators have made extracts of the subneural gland of tunicates, or of the complex composed of the subneural gland and the closely associated ganglion, and have tested such preparations for gonadotropic action mostly in sexually immature mice. Although results for such tests have varied considerably, none has been reported as conspicuously positive and for the most part they have been found questionable or negative. Such tests, however, for the action of proteinaceous hormones, between such distantly related animals have not proven too successful as a rule, even when applied to coldblooded vertebrates and mammals.

Also, gonadotropic responses that involve cellular growth, vitellization, etc. in the invertebrates and lower vertebrates may require weeks or even months to complete. These were among the considerations that prompted surgical removal of the subneural gland and ganglion in tunicates as a means of determining their possible gonadotropic functions.

QUESTION: I am wondering what type of bio-assays have been followed in working with the extracted estrogens obtained from lower forms, or whether it was purely chemical extractions?

ANSWER: We used both biological and chemical methods for the identification of these substances. The Astwood method was the biological test used most for the estrogens as it proved very sensitive and accurate when carefully standardized on our colony of inbred rats. Also, the minimal amount of a preparation required for an Astwood unit, when tested for its ability to promote uterine growth in a period of 30 hours, gave some idea of the kind of estrogen being tested. Those of particular interest were estradiol-17β, estrone, and estriol, and these give very characteristic responses with respect to the uterine growth produced by an Astwood unit within 30 hours.

We also isolated and identified these substances by chemical means. Our fractions, after partial purification, were passed through a countercurrent machine which had been carefully standardized to solutions of authenic estrogens. This was done at least once before the different fractions were also subjected to paper chromatography, in two or more solvent systems.

Our procedures for the isolation of progesterone were of a similar nature and our preparations were tested biologically by the Hooker-Forbes method.

It also should be mentioned in this connection that the amount of steroid hormone per unit wet weight of gonadal tissue varies widely among the different species. In general, they were found in very small amount in the invertebrates, there being only about one or two micrograms of estradiol-17β per kilogram of ovarian tissue in the sea urchins and starfish studied and about 10 times this amount in the pectin. There are very much greater concentrations of estrogens among the vertebrates, and especially is this true among those in which a theca interna is well developed about the ovarian follicle. In certain instances in which sufficient material was obtained, infrared spectrographs were made. An example of this were the spectrographs shown during the lecture which were taken from material obtained from the spiny dogfish, *Squalus suckleyi.*

QUESTION: You mentioned several times that progesterone is the precursor of estrogen. How far down the series have you found progesterone?

ANSWER: We found progesterone in the ovaries of all animals studied, so it must be of common occurence among animals.

QUESTION: You mentioned progesterone is found throughout the animal kingdom. My question is, have any of the biochemists isolated any of the enzyme systems which convert progesterone to estrogens?

ANSWER: Dr. Bickoff is much better qualified than I am to discuss this. I have had no direct experience, but my biochemical associates speak as though this is well established in mammals, and these are the chief animals with which they are concerned. We know very little about such enzyme systems in invertebrates. However, it is of interest that in the invetrebrates and cold-blooded vertebrates that when estradiol-17β is found, progesterone also is found, and when estradiol-17β is present in considerable amount, estrone is also found. From what is now known, it would seem odd to find estrogens in an animal and not progesterone. Also, it would be equally interesting if estrogens were found in the absence of androgens; the reverse, however, though unusual may not be surprising since androgens precede estrogens in the generally conceived metabolic series. It seems to me that the opinions held by the biochemists regarding these matters are well founded, as they apply to the higher vertebrates, but little is known about steroid hormones and related enzyme systems in the lower forms.

Question: Does the subneural gland regenerate?

Answer: It should be mentioned that our observations were limited to one species of tunicate, *Chelyosoma productum*. When the subneural gland was completely removed no regeneration was observed within about 14 months. Even when a fragment of the gland remained after an operation it seemed to heal without pronounced regeneration.

Question: Another question was concerned with the trophocytes of insects. Is there any indication that these produce steroids?

Answer: In reference to this I mentioned that they contained droplets of lipoidal material that might contain steroids. I am not aware of convincing evidence that a particular steroid is present in the trophocytes but it seems quite possible that steroids could be contained in the lipoidal material. (See Bonhag, 1958.)

Question: Which is the lowest form you have tested?

Answer: Echinoderms and mollusks. These are not at the bottom of the phylogenetic series but they are very ancient groups.

Question: Have you been able to find other metabolites of the two hormones you are looking for, for instance, pregnandiol which seems to be almost one relationship?

Answer: The purpose of our study was the distribution of certain steroidal hormones, estrogens, and progesterone—and in our pursuit of these we passed by many interesting substances without finding out what they were. It is quite possible that some of these compounds might have been steroids.

Question: From a general evolutionary standpoint is there any possible correlation between echinoderms that excrete phosphocreatin and any of these female hormones?

Answer: We have no information about this.

REFERENCES

Bonhag, P. F., 1955. Histochemical studies of the ovarian nurse tissue and oöcytes of the milk-weed bug, *Oncopeltus fasciatus* (Dallas). II. Sudanophilia, phospholipids and cholesterol. J. Morph., *97:* 283-312.

Bonhag, P. F., 1958. Ovarian structure and vitellogenesis in insects. Ann. Rev. Ent., *3:* 137-160.

Botticelli, C. R., F. L. Hisaw, Jr., and H. H. Wotiz, 1960. Estradiol-17β and progesterone in ovaries of starfish (*Pisaster ochraceous*). Proc. Soc. Exp. Biol. and Med., *103:* 875-877.

Botticelli, C. R., F. L. Hisaw, Jr., and H. H. Wotiz, 1961. Estrogens and progesterone in the sea urchin (*Strongylocentrotis franciscanus*) and pecten (*Pecten hericius*). Proc. Soc. Exp. Biol. and Med., *106:* 887-889.

Brambell, F. W. R., 1926. The oögenesis of the fowl (*Gallus bankiva*). Trans. Roy. Soc., *214B:* 113-151.

Bullough, W. S., 1955 .Hormones and mitotic activity. Vitam. and Horm., *23:* 261-292.

Butanandt, A., and H. Jacobi, 1933. Über die Darstellung eines krystallisierten pflanzlichen Tokokinins (Thelykinins) und seine Identifizierung mit dem a-Follikelhormon. Z. physiol. Chem., *218:* 104-112.

Chopra, H. C., 1960. Cytological and cytochemical study of the growing oöcytes of the fish, *Boleophthalmus dussumerii.* La Cellula, *60:* 301-318.

Cooper, R. S., 1948. A study of frog egg antigens with serum-like reactive groups. J. Exp. Zool., *107:* 397-437.

Dean, F. O., and I. C. Jones, 1959. Sex steroids in the lungfish (*Protopterus annectens* Owen). J. Endocrin., *18:* 366-371.

Dodd, J. M., P. J. Evennett, and C. K. Goddard, 1960. Reproductive endocrinology in cyclostomes and elasmobranchs. Symp. Zool. Soc. London, No. 1, pp. 77-103.

Flickinger, R. A., and D. E. Rounds, 1956. The maternal synthesis of egg yolk proteins as demonstrated by isotopic and serological means. Biochim. et Biophys. Acta, *22:* 38-42.

Glass, L. E., 1959. Immuno-histological localization of serum-like molecules in frog oöcytes. J. Exp. Zool., *141:* 257-282.

Hagan, H., 1951. *Embryology of the Viviparous Insects.* New York, The Ronald Press Co.

Hisaw, F. L. Jr., C. R. Botticelli, and F. L. Hisaw, 1962. The relation of the cerebral ganglion-subneural gland complex to reproduction in the ascidian, *Chelyosoma productum.* Amer. Zool., *2:* 415.

Hyman, L., 1940. *The Invertebrates.* Volume I: *Protozoa Through Ctenophora.* New York and London, McGraw-Hill Book Company, Inc.

Hyman, L., 1951. *The Invertebrates.* Volume II: *Platyhelminthes and Rhynchocoela.* New York and London, McGraw-Hill Book Company, Inc.

Kemp, N. E., 1956. Electron microscopy of growing oöcytes of *Rana pipiens.* J. Biophysic. and Biochem. Cytol., *2:* 281-292.

Knight, P. T., and A. M. Schechtman, 1954. The passage of heterologous serum proteins from the circulation into the ovum of the fowl. J. Exper. Zool., *127:* 271-304.

Layne, D. S., R. H. Common, W. A. Maw, and R. M. Fraps, 1958. Presence of oestrone, oestradiol and oestriol in extracts of ovaries of laying hens. Nature, *181:* 351-352.

Odor, D. L., 1960. Electron microscopic studies on ovarian oöcytes and unfertilized tubal ova in the rat. J. Biophysic. and Biochem. Cytol., *7:* 567-574.

Payne, F., 1932. A study of the cytoplasm in insect ova. J. Morph., *53:* 523-592.

Pickford, G. E., and J. W. Atz, 1957. *The Physiology of the Pituitary Gland of Fishes.* New York, New York Zoological Society.

Skarzynski, B., 1933. Recherches sur les corps oestrogènes d'originine vegetale. Bull. intern. acad. polon. sci., classe sci. math. nat., BII, 347-353. [C. A., 28, 4755 (1934)].

Sotelo, J. R., and K. R. Porter, 1959. An electron microscope study of the rat ovum. J. Biophysic. and Biochem. Cytol., *5:* 327-341.

Telfer, W. H., 1960. The selective accumulation of blood proteins by the oöcyte of Saturniid moths. Biol. Bull., *118:* 338-351.

Telfer, W. H., 1961. The route of entry and localization of blood proteins in the oöcytes of Saturniid moths. J. Biophys. and Biochem. Cytol., *9:* 747-759.

Trujillo-Cenóz, and J. R. Sotelo, 1959. Relationships of the ovular surface with follicle cells and origin of the zona pellucida in rabbit oöcytes. J. Biophysic. and Biochem. Cytol., *5:* 347-350.

Wotiz, H. H., C. R. Botticelli, F. L. Hisaw, Jr., and A. G. Olsen, 1960. Estradiol-17β, estrone, and progesterone in the ovaries of dogfish (*Squalus suckleyi*). Nat. Acad. Sci., *46:* 580-583.

Wotiz, H. H., C. R. Botticelli, F. L. Hisaw, Jr., and Ira Ringler, 1958. Identification of estradiol-17β from dogfish ova (*Squalus suckleyi*). J. Biol. Chem., *231:* 589-592.

Yamamoto, K., 1957. Studies on the formation of fish eggs XI. The formation of a continuous mass of yolk and the chemical nature of lipids contained in it in the oöcyte of the flounder, *Liopsetta obscura*. J. of the Faculty of Science Hokkaido University. Series VI, *13:* 344-351.

Hormones and Reproductive Behavior of the Poikilothermous Vertebrates

W. S. HOAR
Department of Zoology
University of British Columbia

TIMING and control of the major events of reproduction are dependent on cyclical activity in the neuroendocrine system. External environmental stimuli or—among the more advanced groups—internal physiological rhythms, periodically activate neurosecretory cells in the brain and thus initiate a somewhat variable series of activities which govern the production of gametes and the sexual behavior of animals. Among the vertebrates, pituitary secretion of gonadotropins is linked with steroid secretions of the gonads, so that five or more chemicals play on the various organs and structures to produce the coordinated activities of reproduction.

This pattern of control is now recognized from the cyclostomes to the most highly organized of the mammals (Parkes, 1960). The major components of the regulating mechanism are shown in Figure 1. Further discussion of the basic facts is unnecessary. Within this framework, however, there is still the greatest of uncertainty concerning interconnecting events—both physiological and phylogenetic.

In a detailed analysis of the scheme presented in Figure 1, an attempt might be made to establish the linking physiological connections. Ultimately, many of the mechanisms must depend on particular chemical compounds and it is theoretically possible that the relationships may be very specific—like an enzyme-substrate or an antigen-antibody reaction. This sort of relationship has been sought but never conclusively demonstrated. The nearest approach seems to be the spawning reflex displayed by *Fundulus* rather promptly following the injection of neurohypophyseal hormones (Wilhelmi, et al., 1955) or the development of sex-

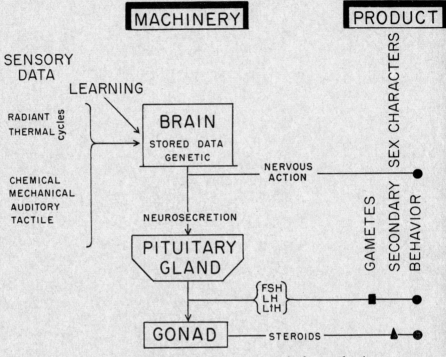

Figure 1. Basic neuroendocrine control of reproduction.

ual behavior after the implantation of stilbestrol dibutyrate in the posterior hypothalamus of the ovariectomized cat, although, in the latter case, the minimum response time was about four days (Harris, et al., 1958).

In most investigations, a less specific relationship between endocrine and motor activity has been found. Students of mammalian psychoendocrinology have usually concluded that neurosecretions and hormones only increase the sensitivity of receptor mechanisms and neural pathways or control their differentiation. In this way, the hormones act as chemical sensitizers rather than specific releasers of behavior patterns. Beach (1945, 1958) in many papers stresses the complexity, both at the neuroendocrine and the motor level and, consequently, the improbability of simple straight-line connections.

In the mammals, at any rate, it is unlikely that any of the elements of reproductive behavior depends on a single hormone and, in the broad outline presented in Figure 1, we may anticipate a complex interconnecting physiology between each of the major levels. At the moment, there is little to indicate that the controls are any simpler at the lower levels of phylogeny.

An understanding of the regulatory mechanisms may also be sought in terms of phylogeny. Details of reproductive behavior vary considerably and show definite evolutionary trends in closely related groups of animals. In ts fullest expression, there is complex pre-breeding behavior involving migration, territorial, and aggressive activities, while breeding behavior itself includes nest building, defence of territory, courtship, mating, and parental care. In many species, some of these elements are omitted. Aggressive behavior may be absent and the contacts between the two sexes reduced to a minimum.

There are now excellent comparative descriptions for many of the vertebrate groups. Studies of the cichlids (Baerends and Baerends van Roon, 1950), the sticklebacks (van Iersel, 1953; Morris, 1958), the anabantids (Forselius, 1957a), and the darters (Winn, 1958a, b) may be mentioned as examples of detailed analyses in fish. Among the Amphibia, evolution of the courtship of salamanders was depicted by Noble (1931) and that of the Anura by Jameson (1955). Many of the reptiles have also been studied. Some of the most detailed of these investigations are those of Noble and his associates more than 20 years ago on the Lacertilia (Noble and Bradley, 1933; Greenberg and Noble, 1944; Evans, 1955). We shall not go farther up the phylogenetic tree.

The point emphasized is that the recording of reproductive activities in a comparative way has gone much farther than the analysis of the controlling events. It seems reasonable to assume that evolution will have produced variety in neuroendocrine control as well as in the motor activities and that interesting and instructive facts will be revealed when these are carefully examined. At present, this is almost a virgin field of research. Only broad generalizations are now possible and these are based almost entirely on the mammal.

Beach (1958) has pointed out that sexual behavior becomes progressively less dependent on humoral control with increasing encephalization. From the rodents and the lagomorphs to the carnivors and thence to the primates, there is less and less dependence on gonadal secretions and more and more dependence on cortical control of mating behavior. Such a trend is probably associated with the relative learning abilities of these groups of mammals. These animals learn readily and much of their behavior is modified by experience. In man, there are few purely instinctive activities—in the sense of innate behavior patterns—and it is well-known that sexual behavior may continue for many years after the gonads have ceased to function.

The general situation is quite the reverse at the lower levels of phylogeny. Behavior is largely innate and reproductive patterns are often fully established without prior experience. Hormones might be expected to control events more rigidly in these groups. Aronson (1958) has examined the evidence and concluded that there is no particular phylogenetic trend in the direction of increased neural control among the poikilothermous vertebrates. However, he is cautious concerning generalizations until more is known of the comparative neurology and endocrinology.

It should be remembered that encephalization is only one of the phylogenetic trends found among the vertebrates. Although there are presently no indications of an evolutionary sequence in neuroendocrine mechanisms related to sexual behavior, much more research will be necessary before any firm conclusions are possible.

The behavior of an animal (whether innate or learned) is based on its genetic constitution. In the case of sexual behavior, genetic aspects are particularly interesting since patterns of behavior are bisexual. The parts played by the male and the female are often quite different and yet, under certain conditions, the motor acts appropriate to one sex may be performed by the opposite sex. The extent to which bisexual behavior patterns are controlled by hormones and the extent to which they are fixed in the neural mechanisms by the genetic code has rarely been explored outside the mammals. It is possible that some of the motor patterns of sexual behavior may be strictly controlled by the genes characteristic of one sex.

In *Drosophila*, certain elements of courtship behavior have been related to a single gene (Bastock, 1956) and, although such direct relationships are not expected among the vertebrates, a complete understanding of the control of sexual behavior will be in terms of genetics as well as physiology and evolution. Anthony (1959) has provided a useful summary of the current understanding of regulatory mechanisms influencing sexual behavior of mammals.

The present discussion is confined largely to the cold blooded vertebrates. In a sense, their behavior is no less complex than that of the higher vertebrates, for it usually involves a pairing of the sexes and frequently such activities as nest building, parental care, and, in some cases, viviparity. It is, however, largely instinctive and, consequently, often devoid of the modifying effects of experience. For this reason

it may prove easier to sort out the controlling physiological mechanisms and the basic phylogeny.

The complexity of reproductive behavior among the lower vertebrates is exemplified in Table 1 based on the teleost fishes. Although parthenogenesis—if it does, in fact exist (Gordon, 1957)—and hermaphroditism are most certainly secondarily evolved, one might expect such animals to operate with minimal endocrine controls. However, this is probably far from the truth. The evidence for parthenogenesis is insufficient to warrant discussion (Spurway, 1953; Gordon, 1957) but hermaphroditism is the established way of life in some species of two different families of teleosts—the Sparidae and the Serranidae (van Oordt, 1933; D'-Ancona, 1949; Reinboth, 1962).

The behavior is complex. Clarke (1959) has described it in *Serranellus subligarius*. This animal, at least in an aquarium, may display by itself and shed eggs and sperm capable of normal fertilization and development without the presence of another partner. On the other hand, there may be an elaborate interplay between two or more individuals with one member of the pair or group (the active initiating fish) assuming quite a different color from the others. Even more amazing, however, the different members of the group may reverse their appearance and roles from time to time during a particular mating activity. It is hard to imagine a control in terms of androgens and estrogens associated with bisexual play.

The teleosts present similar difficulties on a genetic level. In closely related species, it is sometimes the male and sometimes the female who is the

Table 1. Reproductive behavior in some teleost fishes

| | Activities | | | | Courtship | | | | | |
| | | | Nest building | | | Copulation | | Parental care | | |
Conditions	Aggregation—Migration	Territoriality	♂	♀	Bisexual play	Sperm to ♀	Eggs to ♂	♂	♀	Examples
rthenogenetic (?)	—	—	—		—	—		—		Lebistes[1]
rmaphroditic	—	+	—		—	—		—		Serranellus[2]
	+	+	—		+	—		—		
No pair formation	+	—	—		—	—		—		Richardsonius[3] Roccus[4]
Pair formation	+	—	—		+	—		—		Mugil[5] Notropis[6]
	+	+	—	+	+			—		Salmo[7]
	+	—	—	—	+	+	—	—		Lebistes[8, 9]
	+	+	+		+	—		+		Gasterosteus[8]
	+	—	—		+		+	+		Siphostoma[8]
	+	+	+	+	+	—		+		Tilapia[10]
	+	+	+	+	+			+	+	Geophagus[10]

(left margin bracket label: Dioecious)

[1] Spurway (1953) ; [2] Clark (1959) ; [3] Weisel and Newman (1951) ; [4] Woodhull (1947) ; [5] Arn- and Thompson (1958) ; [6] Harrington (1947) ; [7] Jones and King (1952) ; [8] Norman (1947) ; ark and Aronson (1951) ; [10] Reid and Atz (1958).

active member of the pair in nest building, courtship, and parental care; or both males and females may cooperate in these activities. Data for some of the cichlid fishes are summarized in Table 2. As yet, associated differences in neuroendocrine mechanisms have not been described or even investigated.

It is questionable whether generalized controlling mechanisms will be found to operate over the varied range of sexual activities listed in Table 1. Rather, it is suggested that the basic neuroendocrine control (Figure 1) was fully established in the most primitive of the truly vertebrate animals. This is not too dangerous a speculation, since such controls have now been found in all of the modern vertebrates and a comparable neuroendocrine regulation is well-known in many of the invertebrates (Turner, 1960).

Within this general framework, there may be little chemical similarity in the linking mechanisms of different species. Controls may have been variously established during evolution as have the techniques by which eggs and sperm are brought together and protected to the best advantage of the species. Before attempting to discuss this speculation or seeking further generalizations beyond those depicted in Figure 1, some recent studies of the reproductive endocrinology of the male three-spined stickleback (*Gasterosteus aculeatus*) will be summarized.

Table 2. COMPARISON OF THREE MAJOR TYPES OF ORAL INCUBATION AMONG CICHLID FISHES (REID AND ATZ, 1958)

| Species | Spawning location | Eggs picked up at about | Sex of principal parent | | |
			Preparing egg site	Carrying eggs	Carrying young
Geophagus jurupari	On flat stones	24 hrs.	Male and female	Male and female or female	Male and female
Tilapia macrocephala	Depression on bottom	20-130 seconds	Male and female	Male	Male
Tilapia spp. *Haplochromis* spp.	Depression or other nest on bottom	Less than 1 min. to few mins.	Male	Female or male and female	Female or male and female

Hormones and the Reproductive Behavior
of *Gasterosteus aculeatus.*[1]

The behavior of the male three-spined stickleback has been carefully documented. As the breeding season approaches, the males become progressively more aggressive and attack sticklebacks—of either sex—and other small fish, whenever they are encountered. The silvery coat gradually fades and is replaced by a brilliant red one, particularly marked on the throat and lower portions of the body. The eye assumes a characteristic blue. As these changes are completed the male becomes even more aggressive and territorial. In an aquarium he will frequently kill other sticklebacks of either sex, unless there are many hiding places in the tank.

Nest building then commences in the territory and consists of digging a shallow pit (sand digging), collecting algae and small pieces of debris for the construction of the nest (collecting material), and gluing this material into a crude structure by passing over the nest site and applying the mucus which exudes from the glands in the mesonephros. These mesonephric mucous glands, like the brilliant body colors, are secondary sex characters found only in males at the time of sexual activity. Further details of nest construc-

tion will be found in the literature (Tinbergen, 1951; van Iersel, 1953; Guiton, 1960).

Nest building is followed by well-marked courtship activities (zigzag dance) in which the female is led to the nest and spawning takes place. The male incubates the eggs (fanning) and exercises a measure of parental care. These activities are distinct and obvious to any careful observer. They can be quantified and studied in relation to the classical manipulations of the endocrinologist.

As yet, it has not been possible to hypophysectomize sticklebacks in sufficient numbers to do critical work with the surgically hypophysectomized animal. It is possible, however, to obtain animals in which the pituitary gonadotropic activity is low or high through the control of photoperiods and temperature.

Baggerman (1957) showed that sticklebacks maintained under long (16 hour) days—following a short photoperiod regime—would build nests in 30 days or less. On the other hand fish maintained under short (8 hour) photoperiods, unless they had been previously primed, would not become sexually mature in a very long time (8 months or more). Fish which were building nests would become sexually quiescent in about 45 days if the photoperiod was shortened and thereafter showed no further nest building. Our findings are in general agreement (Hoar, 1962) and it is concluded that the pituitary gonadotropic activity remains low under a short daily photoperiod (8 hours) and high under a long

[1] Original data presented here are in part based on unpublished research done in the Department of Zoology and Comparative Anatomy at Oxford. It is a pleasure to thank the Guggenheim Foundation, which sent me to Oxford, The Fisheries Research Board of Canada, and the National Research Council of Canada for research support. I am also indebted to Professor Sir Alister Hardy and Dr. Niko Tinbergen and his associates at Oxford.

daily photoperiod (16 hours). In this way physiologically hypophysectomized animals have been compared with those in which the gonadotropic activity of the pituitary is under stimulation.

Gonadectomy is a simple operation in the immature male and can also be carried out with care in the mature male and the female. Our operation differs from Baggerman's (1957). We use a small incision on each side of the animal and find that sutures are usually unnecessary. Details are given elsewhere (Hoar, 1962).

Gonadectomy in the pre-nest building aggressive phase. Sticklebacks were captured in ponds near Oxford, England, on April 30 and the males were gonadectomized within the next 48 hours. Two gonadectomized males were placed with two normal females in each aquarium. Nine groups (18 castrates) were maintained under 16-hour daily photoperiods and 8 groups (16 castrates) under 8-hour daily photoperiods.

At the time of capture these fish were becoming sexually mature and the males could be distinguished by the orange erythrophores on their throats and the general darkening of their body color. It was, however, 15 days before nest building was first observed in unoperated males collected at this time and maintained under optimal light conditions.

In both photoperiod groups, the developing nuptial colors of the castrated males gradually regressed and the silvery guanine coat characteristic of immature and female fish appeared. These changes were complete within three weeks. The dependence of nuptial coloration on the gonadal hormones

has been noted by other workers (Ikeda, 1933; Baggerman, 1957).

The behavior of the two photoperiod groups was markedly different. None of the gonadectomized males showed any elements of reproductive behavior, but pre-nest building aggressive behavior was maintained and intensified in the fish under 16 hour days while the short-day photoperiod fish became progressively less aggressive and reverted to a condition characteristic of winter fish. Five levels of aggressive behavior are distinguished in this study ranging from 0 (no attacks, fish schooling or aggregating) to IV in which territoriality is marked by definite dominance-subordination relationships; territorial boundaries are sharp and subordinate fish are frequently killed if adequate cover is not provided. Fish are also territorial at level III, but there is no particular dominance on the part of the territorial fish. Levels I and II are based on number of attacks, with 20 or fewer in a 10-minute observation period in the first case and more than that in the second. There are no territories, dominance, or subordination in aquaria categorized as level I or II.

Quantitatively, the castrated males maintained under long photoperiods from the pre-nest building aggressive phase showed almost maximal aggressive behavior. After 30 days, seven of the nine groups were scored level IV while the other two were level III. Eight groups of control, unoperated fish, under like photoperiod conditions were all in stage IV so that it cannot be said that the testis had no effect whatever. Under short photoperiods, by contrast, only two of the eight groups of castrates were scored IV, with one in stage III, two in each of the stages I and II and one at 0. Four groups of unoperated controls held under 8-hour photoperiods were in stages I, III (2 groups), and IV. Qualitatively the differences were obvious and the fighting was always less intense, territories less well-marked, and activity of a lower order under the short photoperiods. There seems to be little doubt that pre-nest building aggressive behavior is dependent on the high level of pituitary gonadotropins, and that the testis has very little to do with the initial springtime development of territoriality in the stickleback.

Gonadectomy in the sexual phase. Seven sexually active males were gonadectomized. One was sand-digging, the others were gluing their nests and two of these showed courtship (zig-zag dances) and displacement fanning. The fish were observed frequently during the day of the operation and at regular intervals for several weeks thereafter, but—with one exception— reproductive behavior was never seen. The one exceptional castrate did show displacement fanning within the first 5 minutes after being returned to the aquarium but never thereafter. Sham operated animals did not show reproductive behavior during the day of the operation but within 24 hours their behavior seemed unaffected by the operation. It seems clear that nest building and associated behavior disappears promptly with the removal of the testis and must depend, to a large extent, on this organ or its secretions.

The aggressive behavior of my fish, gonadectomized in the sexual phase, was not studied. In the initial experiments, where this was attempted, the unoperated male always killed the op-erated fish before it fully recovered. This was attributed to the weakened condition of the fish following the operation. However, Baggerman (1961) finds that the aggressive behavior along with the other elements of sexual and nest building behavior disappears with gonadectomy. She states, "when I castrate males in the second week of the reproductive period, there is a decrease in aggressive activities within one or two days after the operation from 100-150 down to 10-30 per 15 minute period and this level is maintained for at least 10 weeks." This decline is parallel to the decline which occurs when the male rather suddenly ceases to show interest in the nest at the end of the normal reproductive period. Thus, Baggerman's findings indicate that pre-nest building aggressive behavior and the aggressive behavior of the sexual phase are under rather different endocrine controls.

Treatment of castrates with gonadal steroids. The fish which were gonadectomized in the pre-nest building phase and maintained for 30 days under the two different light regimes (see above) were then immersed in solutions of methyl testosterone. The steroid (B.D.H. pure reagent) was added to the aquarium water to produce a concentration of about 1 : 4,000,000. Details of the treatment are given elsewhere (Hoar, 1962). The groups of fish were observed five times per week and as soon as nest building was established, as evidenced by active gluing, the sexually active gonadectomized fish were removed, carefully autopsied, and preserved for histological study. No evidence of testis regeneration was found in these fish.

The androgen treatment stimulated nest building in many of the gonadectomized males, but the results were quite different under the short and long photoperiod regimes. This points to the importance of an interaction between the pituitary gonadotropins and the gonadal steroids in the control of reproductive behavior.

In detail, androgen treatment commenced with 18 gonadectomized fish under the long photoperiod regime and 16 under the short daily photoperiod. Under the long photoperiods, 2 of the castrates died during the next month and 14 (87.5%) built nests; under the short photoperiods, 2 fish also died but only 8 (57%) built nests. The differences between the two groups are even more marked when the "times to nest building" for the individual fish are considered.

Under the long day regime, the first fish to become sexually active built a nest after only 3 days of treatment as against 17 days for the first nest building under the short photoperiod. By the time the first fish made a nest under the short photoperiod regime, more than 50% of the castrates under the longer photoperiods had built nests. The "days to nest building" in the 16-hour photoperiod fish were: 3, 5, 6, 9, 10 (4 fish), 13, 15, 19, 20, 24, and 31—a total of 14 fish when the experiment was terminated. Under the 8-hour treatment, the days to nest building were: 17, 20, 22, 27 (2 fish), 28, 31, and 32—a total of 8 fish. The experiment was discontinued at 32 days when none of the fish in either group looked as though it would make a nest in the next few days. It evidently took twice as long to induce nest building in the physiologically hypophysectomized fish.

The level of aggressive behavior was recorded in these groups during the course of the androgen treatment. In general, results are in accord with those already described. The level remained relatively high in the 16-hour fish and much lower in the 8-hour groups. In the latter groups, nest building *sometimes* occurred with little or no territorial behavior and an active male would sometimes be busy collecting nest material and gluing it into a nest with other fish in close proximity, showing little evidence of territoriality.

In a series of experiments, unoperated fish maintained for a long time under short photoperiods were also treated with androgens. These experiments are considered in detail elsewhere (Hoar, 1962). The results were in full agreement with those just described. All of the fish (males and females) assumed the red color and developed the mucous glands characteristic of the sexually active male but only 4 out of 21 (19%) of the males built nests, and aggressive behavior was even lower than that of the controls under the same photoperiod. This latter result is indicative of a suppression of the already low pituitary activity due to a feed-back from the exogenous androgen. Other results confirm this suggestion (Hoar, 1962).

Androgen treatment of the female fish. In all of the experiments referred to above, some unoperated female fish were included in the tanks containing the methyl testosterone. These females assumed a color very similar to that of the androgen treated or the naturally mature males. Moreover, the kidney of the female, as well as that of the male, was converted into the mucus-secreting structure characteristic of the sexually active male. Histological changes will not be dealt with here, but they have been quantified by measuring the heights of the tubular epithelia and found to be the same in the two sexes. The male secondary sex characteristics can be induced in either sex through androgen treatment. Can the male reproductive behavior also be divorced from the genetics of the animals?

Gonadectomized females were not studied in the Oxford experiments but 2 unoperated females out of 18 (11%) maintained under 16-hour photoperiods and treated with androgen constructed nests and their activities appeared similar to those of the male. None of the treated females under the short photoperiod regime built a nest.

This work with the female stickleback has been continued in Vancouver by Evelyn Hui. She has carefully compared the behavior of gonadectomized males and females maintained under long (16-hour) photoperiods and treated with methyl testosterone. The findings with gonadectomized males are essentially the same as those already described, although Miss Hui has carried the studies further. She has determined that the gonadectomized and treated male will court (untreated) females in the normal way, will show typical "spawning" when eggs are deposited, and will also exhibit the initial parental fanning behavior at the nest site.

Although male secondary sex characteristics are readily induced in the gonadectomized female treated with androgen, nest building behavior appears only slowly and in a very few fish. In an experiment involving 25 females, only 2 individuals (8%) built nests and these started building 20 days and 30 days after the treatment commenced. By contrast, 15 out of 27 (56%) of the gonadectomized males built nests between 14 and 30 days of treatment.

Other differences between the two sexes were also apparent. Females were less aggressive and although they showed sand digging, collecting material, gluing and fanning, these nest building activities were less intense and courtship has not yet been observed. The hormone-treated ovariectomized animals usually show no response to the introduced female—neither aggressive nor sexual.

Further experiments are in progress and present data have not been analyzed in detail, but Miss Hui has watched these androgen-treated females for many hours (over a period of 2 weeks while they were active in nest building) and tested them many times with sexually mature normal females. They have shown no interest in performing the zigzag dance or any other elements of courtship. We are not yet prepared to say that the female cannot perform this movement. It may be that we have not yet provided the correct releaser situation, although it must be added that castrated and treated males do respond under conditions which seem the same to us. Indications are that the genetics of the female does not permit the zigzag dance.

Summary of the Stickleback Experiments

These experiments indicate that pre-nest building aggressive behavior develops under the influence of the pituitary gonadotropins. In this way, sticklebacks will be dispersed from the winter schools and take fullest advantage of the available space in the establishment of their territories. Although not investigated in this study, the gonadotropins also stimulate the interstitial tissue of the testis and initiate the secretion of gonadal steroids.

Androgen is responsible for the male secondary sexual characteristics and in association with the gonadotropins controls nest building, sexual behavior and parental care. Thus, the endocrinology of reproduction in the stickleback can be dissected into several somewhat differently controlled components: pre-nest building aggressive behavior; morphological sex characteristics; nest building aggressive behavior; and nest building. Indications are that genetic females do not have exactly the same neuromotor machinery as the genetic males. Our present findings are summarized in Figure 2.

Discussion

The stickleback findings will now be compared with some of the recorded data for other poikilothermous vertebrates. As indicated in the stippled blocks of Figure 2, the three major events to be considered are pre-breeding behavior, emergence of the secondary sex characteristics, and reproductive behavior itself.

In the stickleback, pre-nest building aggressive behavior is clearly dependent on a high level of pituitary activity and appears to be a biologically appropriate adaptation. If there are advantages in territoriality, as there certainly seem to be, then the initial scattering and separating of the animals prior to nest building is a logical adaptation. Pre-nest building aggressive behavior seems not to have been considered as distinct from the defence of the nest site or the young in any of the endocrinological studies recorded for the lower vertebrates. However, other elements of pre-breeding behavior, such as migration, may be in the same category, and there is at least one pertinent demonstration of direct pituitary control of migration.

Immature terrestrial newts (*Triturus*) develop a "water drive," migrate to aquatic spawning places, and assume the adult form primarily under the influence of prolactin. Most of these changes can be induced in gonadectomized and hypophysectomized newts, and there seems to be little doubt that the lactogenic hormone plays a key role in this migration and transformation. Chadwick (1941) made the initial discovery. Later work is discussed by Pickford and Atz (1957, p. 268). As in the case of *Gasterosteus*, the work with *Triturus* implicates the pituitary in the initiation of that behavior which must logically precede breeding.

Baggerman's (1957) studies of the stickleback show that indirect tropic controls, which are quite independent of the gonads, may be established in

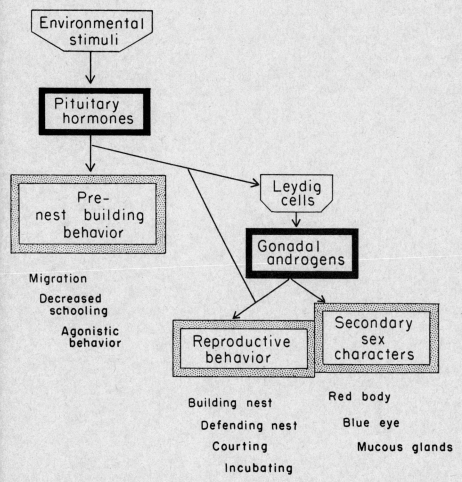

Figure 2. Endocrine control of reproduction in the *Gasterosteus aculeatus* male.

such regulations. In her experiments the pituitary-thyroid axis is implicated in the changing salinity preferences and migration motivation which the stickleback shows even prior to the development of the pre-breeding territoriality which we have studied.

Thus, there are indications that, when the facts are sorted out, the regulation of pre-breeding behavior (migration, territoriality) will be shown to depend strongly on the pituitary hormones and further, that the hormonal basis of pre-breeding aggressive behavior is quite distinct from the defence of a nest or the young.

The androgenic secretions of the testis are known to be active in the development of male secondary sex characters in many animals. In the stickleback, changes can be induced with about equal ease in males and females, and the potentiality for red body, blue eye, and kidney mucous glands has little or nothing to do with the genetics of the particular sex. A similar dependence has been demonstrated in many of the lower vertebrates (Dodd, 1960; Dodd et al., 1960) and in the birds and mammals (Turner, 1960; Beach, 1948, 1958). The only exception to my knowledge is recorded by Witschi (1955) for certain African finches where the pituitary, and not the testes, seems to govern the plumage dimorphism.

Other exceptions may be found, but, at the moment, it can be taken as an almost universal rule that the male morphology is governed by the secretions of the interstitial cells of the testis. Testosterone is considered to be the product of these cells in the mammal (Turner, 1960). This or a similar androgen is probably formed by the testes of all vertebrates. Biochemical differences may eventually be established in different species but comparative data are still meager.

Idler et al. (1960) have isolated 11-ketotestosterone from the plasma of salmon and shown its androgenic activity both in chick comb growth tests (Idler et al., 1961) and in sockeye salmon (Idler, unpublished). It has not been shown, however, that this is the primary product of the salmon testis.

There is much less uniformity in the findings with respect to the endocrinology of sexual behavior. In the stickleback there is clearly a primary dependence on the gonadal secretions, but the gonadal steroid can only exert its full and complete effect in association with a high pituitary gonadotropic activity. Such an interaction of hormones is well known in many endocrine controls (Turner, 1960).

Tavolga's (1955) study of the gobiid fish *Bathygobius soporator* was similar to the stickleback investigation in that the behavior of castrated fish and (surgically) hypophysectomized fish were studied. *Bathygobius* reacted almost diametrically opposite to *Gasterosteus*. Gonadectomy did not impair courtship or spawning by *Bathygobius* but the aggressive behavior was completely abolished. Castrated males showed a reduction in size of the seminal vesicles, indicating an androgenic effect on secondary sex characters, but the male reproductive behavior was unimpaired.

Tavolga's study is not the only one in which fish have continued to show sexual behavior after gonadectomy. Aronson (1951) reported that male *Tilapia macrocephala* lost their yellow opercular colors after gonadectomy but continued to build nests. Sexual activity, involving spawning behavior with normal females, continued when male *Hemichromis* and male *Betta* were gonadectomized (Noble and Kumpf, 1936).

On the other hand, there can be no doubt that, in several species of fish, spawning and nesting behavior disappear immediately with the removal of the testes. *Gasterosteus* was also studied by Bock (1928), Ikeda (1933), and Baggerman (1957) with results similar to ours—at least so far as the initial stages of reproductive behavior are concerned. Likewise, Japanese bitterlings, *Aecheilognathus*, (Tozawa, 1929) and Atlantic salmon, *Salmo salar*, (Jones and King, 1952) lost their spawning behavior after gonadectomy. There seems to be little doubt that sexual behavior in some species of fish is primarily dependent on the gonadal steroids, while in others the pituitary hormones are the prime movers.

Breeding behavior involves a complex series of activities and it is unlikely that they are all coordinated by the same chemicals. Even the rather superficial studies which have already been carried out suggest that different endocrinological controls regulate various components of sexual behavior. In our studies of the androgen-treated female sticklebacks there is an indication that courtship is differently controlled from the earlier nest building activities of breeding. At present, it is not evident whether this difference is neural or endocrine. Again, some exploratory studies of van Iersel (see Baggerman, 1957) suggest that sticklebacks, gonadectomized in the parental phase, will show parental care if they are provided with eggs.

An investigation of the reproductive behavior of the amphibian, *Xenopus laevis* is particularly interesting in this connection. Russel (1955) in a carefully analyzed experiment showed that chorionic gonadotropin facilitates the "clasping" but not the "unclasping" components of mating behavior. He argues strongly for the specificity of hormone action on the central nervous system, and it is to be noted that the different areas of the amphibian brain associated with mating behavior have been mapped (Aronson and Noble, 1945) and the centers associated with clasping and unclasping found to be differently localized.

Finally, there is still a large body of literature concerning hormones and reproduction, which has not been mentioned here. Most of that which pertains to the lower vertebrates is of a general, uncritical nature and does not contribute additionally to the present arguments. Comprehensive reviews are available (Beach, 1948; Pickford and Atz, 1957; Anthony, 1959; Dodd, 1960; Eisner, 1960). Productive lines of research are evident but, at the moment, further understanding awaits careful comparisons based on the proven methods of the ethologist and the endocrinologist.

It is now clear that many of the activities associated with reproduction are strongly dependent on the endocrines. It seems, however, that hormones —both pituitary and gonadal—are associated with the behavior of reproduction in somewhat different ways in the various groups of lower vertebrates. In this, there seems to be nothing at variance with current concepts of endocrinology and evolution. Similar hormones have sometimes been turned to varied functions in different groups of animals, and Darwinian evolution produces compromises as well as neat adaptations with the chemicals and materials available for the processes of natural selection.

Questions and Answers

QUESTION: Is there any variation depending on the concentration of the androgen so far as the female fish is concerned?

ANSWER: We have not been able to go into this very precisely yet, and I think you may have a very good point there. As we all know, you get these feed-back mechanisms. To dump a fish in a concentration of androgen, which probably changes a bit with the amount of vegetation in the tank and all other things that are happening, is a rather crude way of getting at it. It may be that we are suppressing the pituitary activity which is important in bringing this along, as well as the androgen. We have really just made a start in this connection, and we have certain concentrations which we know will do things fairly consistently in the male. All we can say is that the female does not respond as rapidly as the male, either so far as numbers of individuals or so far as activities are concerned. We have made very detailed records of the behavior so that we have the amount of time they spend in fanning and the amount of time they spend in gluing, and we compare all of these elements of behavior. There are a lot of differences in each case between the male and the female.

QUESTION: We found in some of our larger animals that implantation of pellets works very nicely in this respect because the pellets can be recovered so that you have an estimation of the amount of hormones used. Might this give you a more quantitative way to measure the androgen?

ANSWER: We have implanted a few pellets of testosterone and pellets of methyl-testosterone and then recovered and weighed them, but we haven't had the rapid response on the part of the stickleback. We got a very prompt and rather great reaction of the tissue so that the pellet is usually walled off with a lot of connective tissue and debris and the animals don't seem to do as well under this treatment. We have tried to inject suspensions of those materials, both in water and in oil, but the difficulty there is the small size of the animals and the leakage.

QUESTION: What evidence do you have that the effects of the photoperiod are mediated by the pituitary?

ANSWER: I am just wondering whether we have anything you would call real evidence. We are basing this on what is known about the endocrinology of vertebrates in general. There have been some histological studies of the pituitary showing differing amounts of various cells seasonally, seasonal changes in the numbers of different cell types in the pituitary, but under controlled photoperiods. I don't think anyone has examined the pituitaries particularly or provided any really critical data there.

QUESTION: I would like to ask a question with respect to the fish that you spoke of in the beginning. This is the hemaphroditic fish. Does the fish that initiates the action produce a particular product, either sperm or eggs, and do the fish that respond produce either sperm or eggs in particular?

ANSWER: Dr. Clark tried to establish this but was unable to find out whether one particular fish was producing eggs and another sperm. I think the general conclusion was that it seemed likely both products were being produced, but she could not prove this in her article.

QUESTION: In one of your early slides you indicated the influence of neural secretion on pituitary control. I am wondering if perhaps this is hypothetical, based on what we know in birds, or whether you have concrete evidence that shows secretion varies?

ANSWER: There are some histological and histochemical studies of the pituitary of the stickleback. I think neural secretion in general is established there, but again, there has been no attempt made to actually follow enzyme change or other changes in the hypothalamic or various parts of the brain, so far as I know, in the stickleback, nor in fish generally. This hasn't been tackled.

REFERENCES

Anthony, A., 1959. Endocrine control of sexual behavior in mammals. Experentia *15:* 325-328.

Arnold, E. L., and J. R. Thompson, 1958. Offshore spawning of the striped mullet, *Mugil cephalus,* in the Gulf of Mexico. Copeia 1958(2) : 130-132.

Aronson, L. R., 1951. Factors influencing the spawning frequency in the female Cichlid fish *Tilapia macrocephala.* Amer. Mus. Novitates, No. 1484: 1-26.

Aronson, L .R., 1959. "Hormones and reproductive behavior: Some phylogenetic considerations." In *Comparative Endocrinology,* A. Gorbman, ed. John Wiley & Sons, New York, pp. 98-120.

Aronson, L. R., and G. K. Noble, 1945. The sexual behavior of Anura. 2. Neural mechanisms controlling mating in the male leopard frog, *Rana pipiens.* Bull. Amer. Mus. Nat. Hist., *86:* 83-140.

Baerends, G. P., and J. Baerends van Roon, 1950. An introduction to the ethology of Cichlid fishes. Behaviour, Suppl., *1:* 1-243.

Baggerman, B., 1957. An experimental study of the timing of breeding and migration in the three-spined stickleback (*Gasterosteus aculeatus* L.). Arch. Néerland. Zool., *12:* 105-318.

Baggerman, B., 1961. Personal communication. Letter dated February 12, 1961.

Bastock, M., 1956. A gene mutation which changes a behavior pattern. Evolution, *10:* 421-439.

Beach, F. A., 1945. Bisexual mating behavior in the male rat: effects of castration and hormone administration. Physiol. Zool., *18:* 390-402.

Beach, F. A., 1948. *Hormones and Behavior.* New York and London, Hoeber.

Beach, F. A., 1958. "Evolutionary aspects of psychoendocrinology." In *Behavior and Evolution.* A. Roe, and G. G. Simpson, eds. Yale Univ. Press, pp. 81-102.

Bock, F. 1928. Kastration und sekundare Geschlectsmerkmale bei Teleostiern. Z. wiss. Zool., *130:* 455-468.

Chadwick, C. S., 1941. Further observations on the water drive in *Triturus viridescens.* II. Induction of the water drive with the lactogenic hormone. J. Exp. Zool., *86:* 175-187.

Clark, E., 1959. Functional hermaphroditism and self-fertilization in a Serranid fish. Science *129:* 215-216.

Clark, E., and L. R. Aronson, 1951. Sexual behavior in the guppy, *Lebistes reticulatus* (Peters). Zoologica *36:* 49-66.

D'Ancona, U., 1949. Ermafroditismo ed intersessualità nei Teleostei. Experentia, *5:* 381-389.

Dodd, J. M., 1960. "Gonadal and gonadotrophic hormones in lower vertebrates." In Marshall's *Physiology of Reproduction,* Vol. I, Pt. 2. A. S. Parkes, ed. New York, Longmans Green and Co., pp. 417-582.

Dodd, J. M., P. J. Evennett, and C. K. Goddard, 1960. Reproductive endocrinology in cyclostomes and elasmobranchs. Symp. Zool. Soc. London, *1:* 77-103.

Eisner, E., 1960. The relationship of hormones to the reproductive behaviour of birds, referring especially to parental behaviour : a review. Animal Behaviour, *8:* 155-179.

Evans, L. T., 1955. "Group processes in the lower vertebrates." In *Group Processes.* B. Schaffner, ed. New York, Josiah Macy, Jr. Foundation, pp. 268-289.

Forselius, S., 1957a. Studies of Anabantid fishes. I. A qualitative description of the reproductive behaviour in territorial species investigated under laboratory conditions with special regard to genus *Colisa.* Zool. Bidrag. Uppsala, *32:* 93-302.

Forselius, S., 1957b. Studies of Anabantid fishes. III. A theoretical discussion of the differentiation, function, causation and regulation of reproductive behaviour. Zool. Bidrag. Uppsala, *32:* 379-597.

Gordon, M., 1957. "Physiological genetics of fishes." In *The Physiology of Fishes,* Vol. 2. Chap 10. M. E. Brown, ed. New York, Academic Press, pp. 431-501.

Greenberg, B., and G. K. Noble, 1944. Social behavior of the American chameleon (*Anolis caroliensis Voigt*). Physiol. Zool., *17:* 392-439.

Guiton, P., 1960. On the control of behaviour during the reproductive cycle of *Gasterosteus aculeatus.* Behaviour, *15:* 163-184.

Harrington, R. W., 1947. The breeding behavior of the bridled shiner, *Notropis bifrenatus.* Copeia 1947(3) : 186-192.

Harris, G. W., R. P. Michael, and P. P. Scott, 1958. "Neurological site of action of stilboestrol in eliciting sexual behaviour." In *Ciba Foundation Symposium on the Neurological Basis of Behaviour.* London, Churchill, pp. 236-254.

Hoar, W. S., 1962. Hormones and the reproductive behaviour of the male three-spined stickleback (*Gasterosteus aculeatus*). Animal Behavior, *10:* 247-266.

Idler, D. R., P. J. Schmidt, and A. P. Ronald, 1960. Isolation and identification of 11-ketotestosterone in salmon plasma. Can. J. Biochem. Physiol., *38:* 1053-1057.

Idler, D. R., P. J. Schmidt, and J. Biely, 1961. The androgenic activity of 11-ketotestosterone : a steroid in salmon plasma. Can. J. Biochem. and Physiol., *39:* 317-320.

Iersel, J. J. A. van., 1953. An analysis of the parental behaviour of the male three-spined stickleback (*Gasterosteus aculeatus* L.). Behaviour, Suppl., *3:* 1-159.

Ikeda, K., 1933. Effect of castration on the secondary sexual characters of anadromous three-spined stickleback, *Gasterosteus aculeatus aculeatus* (L.). Jap. J. Zool., *5:* 135-157.

Jameson, D. L., 1955. Evolutionary trends in the courtship and mating behavior of Salientia. Syst. Zool., *4:* 105-119.

Jones, J. W., and G. M. King, 1952. The spawning of the male salmon parr (*Salmo salar* Linn. juv.) Proc. Zool. Soc. London, *122:* 615-619.

Morris, D., 1958. The reproductive behaviour of the ten-spined stickleback (*Pygosteus pungitius* L.). Behaviour, Suppl., *6:* 1-154.

Noble, G. K., 1931. The Biology of the Amphibia. New York, McGraw-Hill Book Co., pp. 384-390.

Noble, G. K., and H. T. Bradley, 1933. The mating behaviour of lizards; its bearing on the theory of sexual selection. Ann. N. Y. Acad. Sci., *35:* 25-100.

Noble, G. K., and K. F. Kumpf, 1936. The sexual behavior and secondary sexual characters of gonadectomized fish. Anat. Rec., *67*(Suppl. 1) : 113.

Norman, J. R., 1947. *A History of Fishes,* 3rd ed. London, Benn, 463 pp.

Oordt, G. J. van., 1933. Zur Sexualität der Gattung *Epinephelus* (Serranidae, Teleostei). Z. mikroskop. anat. Forsch. *33:* 525-533.

Parkes, A. S. (ed.), 1960. Marshall's *Physiology of Reproduction*. Vol. I, Part 2. New York, Longmans Green and Co. Ltd., 877 pp.

Pickford, G. E., and J. W. Atz, 1957. *The Physiology of the Pituitary Gland of Fishes*. New York, N. Y. Zoological Society, 613 pp.

Reid, M. J., and J. W. Atz, 1958. Oral incubation in the Cichlid fish, *Geophagus jurupari* Heckel. Zoologica *43:* 77-88.

Reinboth, R. 1962. Morphologische und Funktionelle Zweigeschtlichkeit bei marinen Teleostiern (Serranidae, Sparidae, Centracanthidae, Labridae). Zool. Jahrb. Physiol., *69:*405-480.

Russell, W. M. S., 1955. Experimental studies of the reproductive behaviour of *Xenopus laevis.* I. The control mechanism for clasping and unclasping, and the specificity of hormone action. Behaviour, *7:* 113-188.

Spurway, H., 1953. Spontaneous parthenogenesis in a fish. Nature, *171:* 437.

Tavolga, W. N., 1955. Effects of gonadectomy and hypophysectomy on prespawning behavior in males of the Gobiid fish, *Bathygobius soporator*. Physiol. Zool., *28:* 218-233.

Tinbergen, N., 1951. *The Study of Instinct*. Oxford, Clarendon Press, 228 pp.

Tozawa, T., 1929. Experiments on the development of the nuptial coloration and pearl organs of the Japanese bitterling. Folia Anat. Jap., *7:* 407-417.

Turner, C. D., 1960. *General Endocrinology,* 3rd ed. Philadelphia, W. B. Saunders Co., 511 pp.

Weisel, G. F., and H. W. Newman, 1951. Breeding habits, development and early life history of *Richardsonius balteatus,* a Northwestern minnow. Copeia, 1951(3) : 187-194.

Wilhelmi, A. E., G. E. Pickford, and W. H. Sawyer, 1955. Initiation of the spawning reflex response in *Fundulus* by the administration of fish and mammalian neurohypophysial preparations and synthetic oxytocin. Endocrinology, *57:* 243-252.

Winn, H. E., 1958a. Observations on the reproductive habits of darters (Pisces-Percidae). Amer. Midland Nat. *59:* 190-212.

Winn, H. E., 1958b. Comparative reproductive behavior and ecology of fourteen species of darters (Pisces-Percidae). Ecol. Monogr., *28:* 155-191.

Witschi, E., 1955. Vertebrate gonadotropins. Memoirs Soc. Endocrinol. *4:* 149-165.

Woodhull, C., 1947. Spawning habits of the striped bass (*Roccus saxatilis*) in California waters. California Fish and Game, *33:* 97-102.

Changes in the Endocrine Organs Associated with Lowered Fertility in Cattle*

PERRY T. CUPPS
Department of Animal Husbandry
University of California, Davis

TREATMENT of low fertility or sterility in cattle has been rather unsuccessful, and results from a given treatment for a given type of lowered fertility do not agree. On the assumption that the conflict might be related to differences in cause, we started a series of investigations of histological changes in the endocrine organs related to reproduction. Included were normal and low-fertility animals of both sexes. In the early stages of the study, pituitaries, adrenals, ovaries or testes, thyroids, and pancreas were collected. The thyroids and pancreas proved to be histologically normal, so later investigations were limited to the first four organs.

Animals were from various sources. Many were from the University herd of Jerseys and Holsteins, a majority of them inbred to varying degrees, representing three distinct lines of breeding. Reproductive histories were complete for all of the cows and some of the bulls. Some of the sterile bulls, ob-tained from other sources, were of the Guernsey, Hereford, Angus, and Shorthorn breeds. When breeding records were not available, potential fertility was estimated from semen quality as indicated by percentage of abnormal spermatozoa, percentage motility, and percentage live spermatozoa. Though these tests are not as accurate as a breeding test, they are highly correlated with the demonstrated fertility of animals ranging from sterile to highly fertile.

Low-fertility animals were classified on the basis of several criteria. The tentative classification is arbitrary, and further studies may reveal that certain animals may have to be reclassified or

* This research was financed by grants from the W-49 regional research fund.

that certain groups may need to be subdivided further. The primary basis for classifying cows was their cyclic reproductive behavior combined with histological conditions of the organs at autopsy. The bulls were classified primarily by the characteristics of the semen, with further subdivisions by histological characteristics of the organs. Changes in the adrenal gland, found in many of the low-fertility animals, are reported in Table 1.

Table 1.   CHANGES IN THE ADRENAL GLANDS OF ANIMALS TESTED

Group	No. of animals	Glomerulosa width	Fasciculata and reticularis width[1]
		mm.	*mm.*
Normal cows	20	0.296	2.04
Pregnant cows	9	0.254	2.08
Normal bulls	6	0.30	2.06
Cows with irregular cycles	15	0.371	2.12
Nymphomania (Holstein)	4	0.202	2.34
Nymphomania (Jersey)	5	0.499	2.35
Bulls—normal libido—testicular hypoplasia	5	0.21	1.87
Fascicular tumor	4[2]	0.27	1.29
Adrenal hypertrophy	4	0.40	2.09
Hyaline degeneration of the seminiferous tubules	5	0.40	1.87

[1] Fascicular and reticular width measured together because there is no distinct separation.
[2] Fascicular and reticular width measured in the nontumerous areas.

Measurement of the zonal widths is not a very good way of determining changes but it offers a method of comparing different groups. As shown in the table, the size of the adrenals as measured by zonal width was remarkably constant in normal animals, and the different groups of low-fertility animals showed changes in one or more of the zones. Some of the changes were caused by hypertrophy of the individual cells, and others were the result of hyperplasia. Various combinations of changes were found: in some animals, all zones were affected, whereas in others the changes were confined to one or the other of the zones measured. In some individuals a narrow zone of densely staining cells was found between the glomerulosa and fasciculata (see Figure 12).

Nymphomania

The term nymphomania as applied to cattle designates cows that show constant estrus, short intervals between estrus, or very aggressive sexual behavior toward other animals in a herd. Some cows also show a partial development of a crest, an enlarged clitoris, and a "raised" tail head. Since these latter characteristics are not a feature of the condition in all animals, some confusion has resulted in comparisons of data reported by different investigators. Adrenal virilism and cystic ovarian degeneration have also been used to describe animals showing one or more of the above symptoms. In the animals we studied, two distinct histological conditions were found in the ovaries and adrenals. As shown in Table 1, there was an increased width in the two inner zones of the adrenal in all of the animals. In the Holsteins the glomerulosa was normal in width, but in the Jerseys the glomerulosa was doubled in width. Corpora lutea were absent from the ovaries of four of the animals and present in the other five.

The pituitary, adrenal fasciculata, and an intermediate-sized follicle from a nymphomaniac cow in which corpora lutea were absent from the ovary are shown in Figures 1, 2, and 3, respectively.

In these animals the pituitary was enlarged and the small basophil cells, or delta cells, appeared to be normal and physiologically active. Histologically, it resembled the gland seen in the normal cow during the early stages of the development of the corpus luteum.

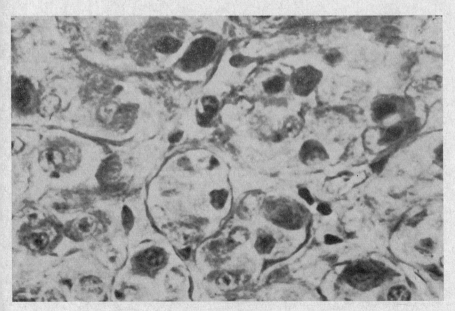

Figure 1. Pituitary from a cow with nymphomania (X 1000). The small basophil cells appear normal and physiologically active.

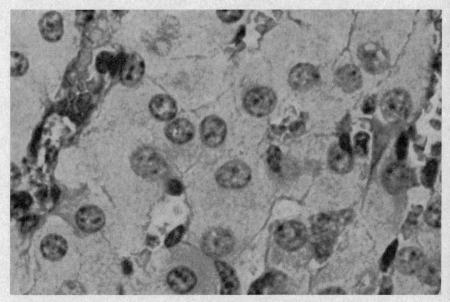

Figure 2. Adrenal fasciculata, nymphomania (X 1000). Notice the hypertrophy of the fasciculata.

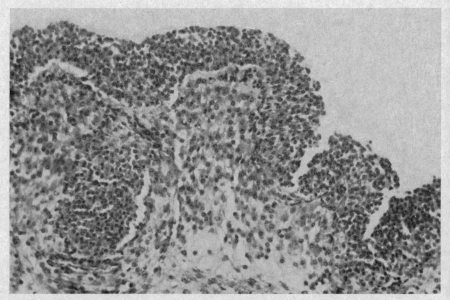

Figure 3. Intermediate sized follicle from the ovary of a cow with nymphomania (X 430). The theca interna is thickened and hyperplastic.

The enlargement of the adrenal was caused by a hypertrophy of the cells of the fasciculata and reticularis (see Figure 2). The difference in the widths of the glomerular zone in the Jerseys and Holsteins remains to be explained.

The small tertiary follicles in the ovaries of these animals were normal histologically, but in follicles about one centimeter in diameter the theca interna was thickened and hyperplastic (see Figure 3). The granulosa appeared to be normal at this stage. In larger follicles there was a degeneration of the cells from the theca interna, and in some follicles of ovulatory size, about 2 centimeters in diameter, it was difficult to find normal interna cells in many parts of the follicle. The granulosa was thinner in these larger follicles than in the smaller follicles, but appeared to be of normal thickness when compared with normal preovulatory follicles.

Individual granulosa cells showed evidence of luteinization at this stage, but did not reach the size found in the early stages of the normally developing corpus luteum. After the follicles reach $2\frac{1}{2}$ centimeters or more in diameter, both cellular layers have degenerated to a great extent, although occasional granulosa cells may be found. The few corpora lutea found in these animals appeared to be larger than normal, but no quantitative data are available to determine whether the apparent increased size is significant.

Testicular Hypoplasia

Testicular hypoplasia has been found in Holstein, Hereford, Jersey, and Shorthorn bulls. In some cases it is congenital, and there is subjective evidence that it may be inherited. The afflicted animals had normal secondary characteristics and normal libido. Their semen was characterized by a low concentration of spermatozoa, averaging 594,000 sperm per cubic millimeter, compared to 1,266,000 for normal bulls. Motility and percentage of live sperm were low, averaging 17% and 36%, respectively. Abnormal spermatozoa were high, averaging 33%, compared to 5% in normal bulls. All types of abnormal sperm are found, including macroheads, pyriform heads, and tightly coiled tails. Fructose and citric acid concentrations were normal.

The small basophilic cells of the pituitaries from these animals were hyalinized, as shown in Figure 4. The large basophilic cells were normal histologically.

The adrenal cortices from these animals were decreased in width (Table 1 and Figure 5), but the cells appeared to be normal histologically.

The testes were smaller and softer than normal. Histologically, the interstitial cells were normal, but many of the tubules were degenerated (Figure 6).

Some tubules were completely degenerated; others showed fairly normal development except that fewer developing cells were present. Many tubules showed arrested spermatogenic development at the primary spermatocyte stage, and others showed faulty development of the spermatocytes in that cytoplasmic division did not occur. The result was multinuclear giant cells

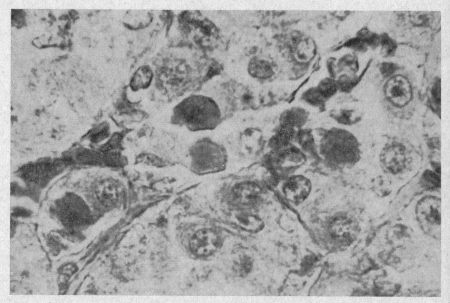

Figure 4. Pituitary of a bull with hypoplasia of the testis (X 1000). The small basophilic cells are hyalinized.

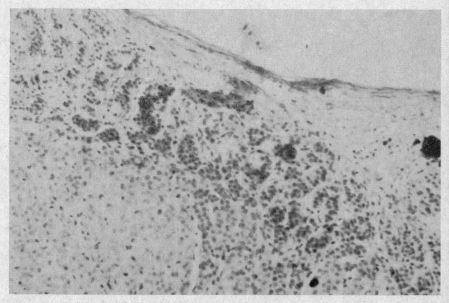

Figure 5. Adrenal from a bull with hypoplasia (X 430). The cortex is decreased in width, but the cells appear normal histologically. Compare this figure with Figure 12.

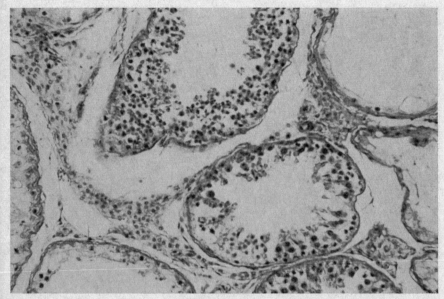

Figure 6. Hypoplastic testis (X 430). The degeneration of some of the tubules is quite marked.

within the lumen of the tubule. With the method of Ortavant (1959)[1] it can be shown that spermatogenesis was arrested at the primary spermatocyte stage. The proportion of tubules showing this abnormality was greater in the animals producing semen with fewer spermatozoa.

Injection of gonadotropins into these bulls increased sperm concentration but did not correct the other poor characteristics of the semen.

Fascicular Tumors

Bulls were placed in the category of fascicular tumors because small nodular tumors were found in the adrenal fasciculata at autopsy (Figure 7). The glomerulosa was of normal width, and the other two zones were narrowed in the nontumorous areas. The semen from bulls with this condition showed some characteristics similar to those of the group with adrenal hypertrophy, though the changes in the adrenal were not identical. This similarity points out the hazards of using this criterion for grouping, and more complete studies will probably lead to further division of these groups. Different breeds were represented in the two groups, and the difference may be related to breed. Also, effects on the semen could be caused by the production of an abnormal steroid, which is not reflected by the anatomical changes in the glands.

[1]Robert Ortavant, 1959. *Reproduction in Domestic Animals,* Vol. II, page 5. New York, Academic Press.

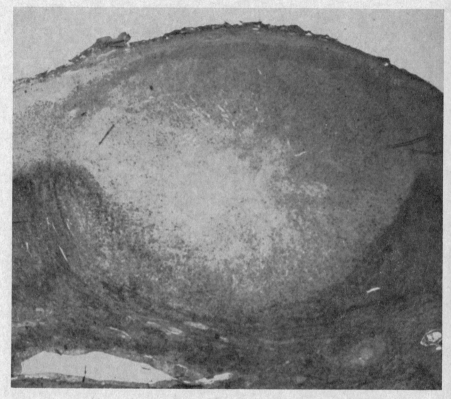

Figure 7. Fascicular tumor of the adrenal (X 20). The glomerulosa is normal in width but the other two zones are narrowed in the nontumerous areas.

The concentration of sperm was high in the semen from three of the four bulls, and low in the other. Motility and percentage of live spermatozoa were low, and two of the animals had been withdrawn from service because their conception rate was below normal. Abnormal spermatozoa were intermediate in number, with the abnormality in a relatively large proportion of them confined to the tail. Libido was normal in three of the bulls, and low in the other. In the bulls with a high concentration of sperm the testes were normal with respect to spermatogenesis. The interstitial tissue was increased in amount, and the individual cells showed hypertrophy (Figure 8). The stages of the cycle of the seminiferous epithelium were as in normal bulls, which indicated that increased sperm production was caused by more cells undergoing spermatogenesis rather than a change in the length of time required for maturation of an individual group of cells.

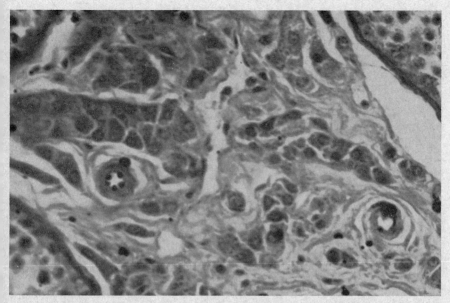

Figure 8. Testis from a bull with adrenal tumor (X 1000). The interstitial tissue is hypertrophied. Indications are that increased sperm production is due to more cells in the tubules undergoing spermatogenisis.

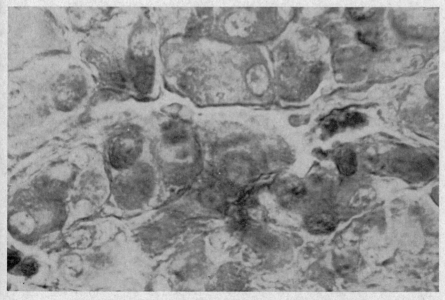

Figure 9. Pituitary from a bull with adrenal tumor (X 1000). The small basophil cells are increased in number and appear to be active.

The small basophil cells of the pituitaries from bulls producing the concentrated semen are shown in Figure 9. These cells were increased in number and appeared to be active.

The fructose concentration was decreased in these bulls, averaging 284 mg. percent, compared to 628 mg. percent in normal bulls. Citric acid concentration was also lower than normal but not decreased as much.

Hyaline Degeneration of the Seminiferous Tubules

Bulls were placed in this group because the first animals studied show a complete degeneration of the seminiferous tubules (Figure 10). This degeneration differed from that found in the bulls with hypoplasia in that spermatogonia were missing in practically all of the tubules. In addition, the basement membrane was thickened; and in some of these animals the walls of the testicular blood vessels were thickened. Small interstitial cell tumors were found in three of the bulls. Grossly, these areas appeared as small yellow nodules in the testis. On histologic examination the nuclei of the nodular cells were pyknotic and the cytoplasm shrunken. Salt consumption was about twice normal in two of the bulls. When supplementary salt was removed from their diet they drank the urine of bulls in adjacent pens. When placed in isolation their salt excretion became balanced with their intake, and they showed no evidence of a sodium deficiency.

The pituitaries from these bulls were normal histologically, as shown in Figure 11.

The glomerulosa of the adrenals from these bulls was abnormally wide (Figure 12 and Table 1). The fasciculata and reticularis were slightly decreased in width. A prominent layer of densely staining cells was measured as glomerulosa, contributing to the increased width. However, the glomerulosa was still wider than normal when this "zone" was excluded. The increased glomerular width appeared to be caused by a true hyperplasia.

The animals in this group were probably at advanced stages of the testicular condition found on autopsy. Some of the animals in the group with adrenal hypertrophy may be in the early stages of this condition. Possibly bulls grouped as having adrenal hypertrophy should be divided and placed either in the group with fascicular tumors or in this group, but our information is not developed enough to make a basis for regrouping them available.

The semen from one of these bulls contained 4,000 sperm per cubic millimeter, and no sperm were present in the other three. Fructose concentration, averaging about 400 mg. percent, was intermediate between that of normal bulls and of bulls with adrenal tumors. Libido was variable, but would be considered normal for dairy bulls of comparable ages. If increased glomerular width and high salt consumption are valid criteria for the early stages of this condition, the testicular degeneration would not be so pronounced. We obtained one bull that appeared to be such an animal. The semen produced by this animal had the following characteristics: motility 50%, concentration

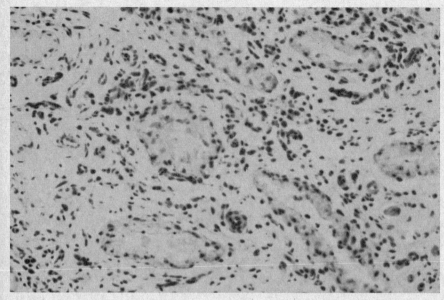

Figure 10. Testis from an aspermic bull (X 430). Complete degeneration of tubules to the extent that spermatogonia are missing in practically all of the tubules; the basement membrane is thickened.

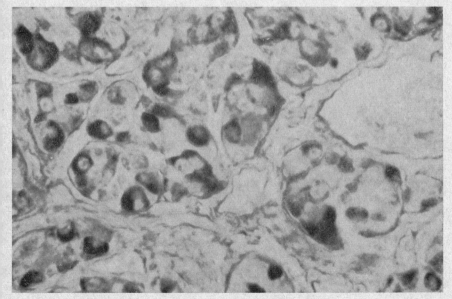

Figure 11. Pituitary from a bull with aspermia (X 630). The pituitary appears normal histologically.

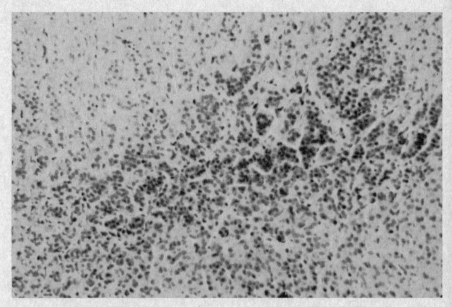

Figure 12. Adrenal from a bull with testicular aplasia (X 430). The glomerulosa is abnormally wide while the other two zones are somewhat decreased in width. There appears to be hyperplasia of the glomerulosa.

620,000 spermatozoa per cubic millimeter, fructose 500 mg. per 100 ml., citric acid 440 mg. per 100 ml., 60% live sperm, and 24% abnormal sperm. Preliminary observations indicate that spermatic degeneration occurred very early in spermatogenesis as shown by degeneration of some of the spermatogonia. Later stages of spermatocytogenesis and spermiogenesis appeared to be normal.

These observations suggest that lowered fertility in cattle results from more than one cause, and that individuals with very similar symptoms may show different histological conditions in the organs. Several features are apparent from the histological conditions reported. In general, when spermatogenic tissue is present in the testis the condition of the small basophilic cells of the pituitary is related to the concentration of spermatozoa in the semen. Furthermore, as estimated by secondary sex characters, the production of sperm is independent of the factors causing the development of the secondary sex characters. Testicular degeneration can occur in the presence of an apparently normal pituitary gland, and the stage at which degeneration occurs is different under these circumstances. There are also indications that in many animals, more than one abnormality may affect the reproductive organs within an individual.

There is a striking similarity between the conditions we found in the bulls and those reported in medicine as "Cushing's Syndrome" and the "Adrenogenital Syndrome," including a salt-losing condition. Since treatment of some of these animals with various hormones caused no striking changes in the semen characteristics, we recently started a group of experiments to attempt to clarify the relationship between the adrenal gland and reproduction in cattle. These experiments consisted of injection of various adrenal steroids into normal and low-fertility bulls, removal of the adrenal with subsequent maintenance therapy, a study of the adrenal metabolites in the excreta, and the incubation of adrenal homogenates followed by extraction and hormone identification.

Injections of hydrocortisone into normal bulls had different effects, depending on the amount used. At low doses of 75 to 300 mg. per week, the concentration of spermatozoa was increased but other characteristics of the semen were not affected. At high doses, 500 to 1,500 mg. per week, spermatozoa concentration was increased and fructose concentration decreased. Other characteristics of the semen were not changed. Supplemental hydrocortisone in a bull with an adrenal tumor increased the sperm concentration further, but had no other effects on the semen. In one bull with glomerular hyperplasia, supplemental hydrocortisone decreased spermatozoa and fructose concentration slightly. In one bull with hypoplasia, spermatozoan concentration was increased.

These results were confusing, to say the least, but since supplemental testosterone had no effect on any of these bulls, the data suggested that adrenal malfunction was related to some of the characteristics found in the animals producing abnormal semen. They further suggested that the adrenal might be producing steroids other than those

essential for life, which were affecting the production of semen.

Adrenalectomy was performed in five bulls. Two died from improper replacement therapy. One was sacrificed when it was established that he had chronic nephrosis. One of the two animals now alive was adrenalectomized at 3 months. With proper therapy, he has been maintained for 18 months and has grown normally. Semen collections were begun when he was 1 year old. The semen is normal except that the concentration of spermatozoa has never been higher than 600,000 per cubic mm. At 21 months, this animal has a crest that is underdeveloped, about the size of a normal animal at 1 year. His horns are growing at a decreased rate, but his libido is normal. Slow horn growth has also been found in a few sterile bulls with adrenal abnormalities.

Another bull, offspring of a cow that had been a nymphomaniac, was grown for the adrenalectomy experiment. Semen, collected from this animal beginning at 1 year of age, had the following characteristics: concentration 500,000 sperm per cubic millimeter, motility 35%, live spermatozoa 54%, abnormal spermatozoa 36%, fructose concentration 150 mg. per 100 ml. A normal bull of the same age produced semen with a sperm concentration of 1,720,000, 70% motility, 77% live, 6% abnormal, and 800 mg. of fructose per 100 ml.

At 18 months of age the bull producing the poor-quality semen was adrenalectomized and placed on corticoid therapy. After he recovered from surgery, semen was collected again. The characteristics of this semen were as follows: concentration 1,290,000 spermatozoa per cubic millimeter, motility 67%, live spermatozoa 74%, abnormal spermatozoa 7%, and fructose 970 mg. per 100 ml. This animal has since been mated to some related females to try to determine if this condition is inherited.

The facts reported above indicate that adrenal cortical secretions are related to normal reproduction and certain types of low fertility in cattle. The relationship appears to be complex, and further experiments will be necessary for complete elucidation of its role in reproduction. In some instances it has been shown to be the primary cause for the production of low-quality semen, and it appears to be related to normal development of secondary sex characteristics. The data suggest that hydrocortisone increases the production of spermatozoa, but different levels have not been used on adrenalectomized bulls, so it is possible that the hydrocortisone may affect the secretion of other steroids, which in turn affect the production of spermatozoa. Histological data suggest that the effect is mediated through the pituitary gland. Supplemental hydrocortisone has a similar effect on normal and adrenalectomized rabbits.

The change in the semen of one bull following adrenalectomy suggests that other steroids from the adrenal may also affect semen characteristics. The type of steroid exerting this effect has not been identified, but some of the characteristics of the semen suggest a physiological effect similar to that of estrogen. However, the development of a small crest in this animal's mother, showing symptoms of nymphomania, suggests an androgenic action. It is possible that the steroid is an intermediate, with both androgenic and estrogenic properties, but this possibility has not been tested experimentally. It was recently shown that the ovaries from cows with nymphomania convert progesterone to $\triangle$ 1,4-androstadiene-3,17-dione. Theoretically this compound should have both estrogenic and androgenic properties. Whether it is present in animals with the condition reported here has not been tested, but it is certainly one of the steroids that should be studied further.

The extensive hyperplasia of the adrenal found in bulls with complete tubular degeneration suggests an increased secretion by the adrenal cortex, but the qualitative and quantitative output of steroids by these glands has not been determined. It has not been established whether the changed activity of the adrenal is the cause of this condition or whether the adrenal is responding to a faulty sodium metabolism by the kidney. Using radioactive carbon 14, we are now studying the excretion of hydrocortisone. When we have established methods of determining adrenal steroids in the excreta, we hope to be able to study the excretion of adrenal steroids in animals with an abnormal appetite for salt.

Questions and Answers

QUESTION (DR. HISAW, SR.): I would like to make a comment, and this probably will pass for a question. I can't help but be struck by the great similarity of the report that Dr. Cupps has just given us and one that you would hear in a clinical report. The gross morphology of the testis and ovary he has reported can be duplicated almost exactly in human material. The work he has done is equally as good, if not better in some respects, as anything that has been done in the clinical studies of human material. We have been hearing a report of a thorough study of the reproductive peculiarities of the ruminant. I suppose in California Cole has about exhausted the horses, and Cupps started on cattle.

DR. CUPPS: I am afraid of the horse, Dr. Hisaw. (Much laughter.)

DR. HISAW: Anyway, it is something that was greatly needed, and you are supplying it in a wonderful fashion.

I also was attracted by some of the remarks made with regard to changes of the follicle in the normal cycle of the cow. Lutienization seems to be the primary process and ovulation occurs incidentally. I was struck by the way it has been shown that in the follicles of cattle lutienization of the granulosa starts in before ovulation.

I must register disagreement with use of the term "thecal lutienization." I tend not to use this expression, probably in response to a feeling that it is not physiologically correct. There is considerable evidence drawn from work on rats and monkeys indicating that the theca interna of the follicle is an endocrine source of estrogen and equally strong indications that it is not of importance in the secretion of progesterone. I would appreciate Dr. Cupps' opinions on this point.

DR. CUPPS: I believe these theca cells secrete estrogen. If one examines the uterus and the vaginal epithelium of a cow at the time the theca cells are enlarging, a definite estrogenic response is seen. Some of the older literature dealing with primate reproductive cycles presents data indicating a distinct rise in the secretion of estrogen approximately 8 to 10 days following ovulation. The secondary rises in estrogen secretion correspond very closely to the enlargement of the "theca lutein" cells, and I hope we will be able to measure the content of estrogen in the corpora lutea during the different stages of the cycle in cattle in the near future. When I used the term "theca luteinization" I was merely repeating the terminology I was taught. I do not think it is correct either and I will be happy to adopt another term when one becomes available.

QUESTION: What are the relationships between genetics and nutrition as far as these conditions are concerned?

ANSWER: We believe that some of these abnormalities are hereditary. This belief is based on the high incidence of the condition in one of the inbred lines and the close relationship between individuals with lowered fertility. We do not think that the nutritional status of these animals is related to the lowered fertility. These animals are dairy animals and in our experience dairy cattle are not usually subjected to adverse nutritional regimes. In beef cattle nutrition may be important; but in dairies under normal management it does not appear to be a very important cause for low fertility.

Physiology of Reproductive Development in Higher Plants

ANTON LANG
Department of Biology
California Institute of Technology

YOU ARE UNDOUBTEDLY familiar with the famous dictum of Gertrude Stein—"a rose is a leaf is a thorn." Are you also aware that Miss Stein was closer to truth than she may have felt and desired? If we analyze her statement botanically, the thorn part is wrong; a thorn is neither a leaf nor a flower. But "a rose is a leaf" *is* basically correct. To the botanist, a rose, like any flower, is a shoot, with leaves borne on a stem. Leaves and stem are thoroughly modified, but not basically different from the leaves and stems of the rest of the rose bush. This is the fact that makes flowering particularly interesting.

When a plant proceeds to reproduction, it does not use organs or structures which have been present much of the time from the beginning of its life, although perhaps in an inactive state; nor does it form something entirely new. It continues producing organs which it has been producing before—leaves and stems—but modifies their size, shape, and pattern of arrangement, so that the net result is a different and novel structure. This is a very interesting, specific type of development, and we would like to know how the plant accomplishes this transformation.

Flower Initiation

In my survey of the physiology of reproductive development in higher plants I will limit myself to the very first event, the inception of the flower as a whole, a process we call *flower initiation,* and shall not speak about later stages of flower development, the formation of individual flower structures (calyx, petals, anthers, and ovaries), the opening of the flower, fertilization, and fruit and seed development. This is partly because we know relatively little about many of these stages, partly because they are less unique than flower initiation, involving growth processes which we also find in the vegetative region of the plant.

Whenever we approach a phenomenon physiologically, one basic premise has to be satisfied; the phenomenon must be accessible to experimental modification. In many plants, flower formation appears to be determined exclusively by internal factors which are difficult to modify. A number of years ago, a young lady at the University of Göttingen in Germany spent her entire work towards the Ph.D. in efforts at preventing one such plant from flowering. She succeeded, too, but each time she did the plant was dead. The story had a happy ending because the young lady did get her degree; however, it is clear that such a plant is poor material for the study of the physiology of flowering.

But, nature, in her wisdom and forethought of problems with which plant biologists might be faced, has created a number of plants in which the situation is different, in which flowering is controlled by certain environmental factors, and is controlled *in a specific manner*. By this latter statement I mean that the plant will germinate, produce leaves, stems, and roots and will perform all its other duties, but it will not flower as long as those particular factors are withheld. Here, then, we have the premise for which we have been searching; we can control flower formation experimentally and can do so in an accurate, predictable, and reproducible manner without directly interfering with other growth processes in the plant.

We know two main factors which control flower formation in this specific fashion. One is a period of *low temperature;* in this case we speak of cold-requiring plants and of *vernalization*. The other is *length of day;* its action is called *photoperiodism.*

Among daylength-dependent or photoperiodic plants, we distinguish two principal groups, the long-day and the short-day plants. Flowering in long-day plants is induced if daily light periods *exceed* a certain, critical minimum; in short-day plants it is induced if daily light periods stay *below* a critical length.

The term "induced" is used deliberately, for daylength—and also low temperature—does have an inductive type of action. By this is meant that in order to cause a response, the causative factor does not have to act until the response is actually consummated —in our case, until flowers have been initiated. It is sufficient for the factor to act for a certain length of time; the response will then take place even if the factor has been removed, and sometimes (in the case of cold requirement) may not take place *unless* it has been removed. Actual time periods for which "our" factors—cold or the proper daylength—have to act vary in very wide limits, depending on the species or variety. In the case of daylength, however, we know some plants which can be induced to flower formation by a single day of the right length.

Let me at this point introduce a few technical terms, namely "inductive" and "noninductive" conditions and thermo- and photoinduction. By inductive conditions we mean those conditions under which the particular plant which we are considering is going to flower; by noninductive those under which it is not. Thus, long days would be inductive for long-day plants and noninductive for short-day plants; short days *vice versa*. Using these terms is much easier and clearer than to speak, e.g., of long-day plants kept in long-day conditions (flowering) or short-day conditions (nonflowering) and short-day plants in long days (nonflowering) or short days (flowering). Thermoinduction is the actual treatment of cold-requiring plants with low temperatures; photoinduction is the corresponding term for photoperiodic plants.

Examples of cold-requiring plants are certain strains of the black henbane (*Hyoscyamus niger*), carrot, many varieties of sugar-beet, the winter or fall varieties of wheat, rye, barley, oats, and many other plants. Examples of long-day plants are other strains of *Hyoscyamus niger*, *Nicotiana sylvestris* (a wild tobacco), dill, many of our summer-blooming annual ornamentals, etc.; among short-day plants, we have the cocklebur (*Xanthium pennsylvanicum*), Biloxi soybean and other soybean varieties, some species of *Bryophyllum*, the Maryland Mammoth variety of cultivated tobacco, *Perilla frutescens*, and the Japanese morning glory (*Pharbitis nil*). Some of these plants have been the main war horses in our experimental efforts, and will be referred to again on numerous occasions throughout my talk.

The first two figures illustrate the behavior of these various plant types.

Figure 1. A cold-requiring variety of *Hyoscyamus,* with cold treatment on the left and without cold treatment on the right (G. Melchers and A. Lang, 1946).[1]

Figure 1 shows plants of a cold-requiring variety of *Hyoscyamus* with cold treatment (left) and without (right); Figure 2 the long-day wild tobacco (*Nicotiana sylvestris*, top) and the short-day Maryland Mammoth tobacco (bottom) in a 16-hour day (left: long-day plant flowering, short-day plant not flowering), and a 10-hour day (right: long-day plant vegetative, short-day plant flowering).

Before proceeding to a discussion of our knowledge of the physiology of cold-requiring, long-day, and short-day plants, I should mention that two additional photoperiodic response types have been described in recent years, the long-short-day and short-long-day plants. As the names imply, these plants have dual daylength requirements which, furthermore, must be satisfied in a particular order. The plants will not flower if kept continuously in long or short days, or if long and short days are applied in the wrong sequence.

---

[1] *Figures 1, 2, 3, 7, and 8 are shadowgraphs drawn from photographs and are thus realistic representations of the responses in question.*

Examples of long-short-day plants are some species of *Bryophyllum* and the night-blooming jasmin (*Cestrum*

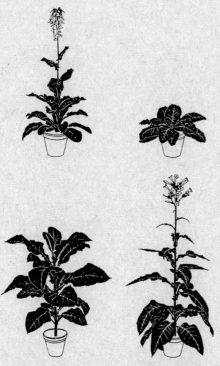

Figure 2. The long-day wild tobacco (*Nicotiana sylvestris*) plant (top) and the short-day Maryland Mammoth tobacco plant (bottom) on a 16-hour day on the left and a 10-hour day on the right (Melchers and Lang, 1946).

nocturnum). The Canterbury bell (*Campanula medium*) and white clover (*Trifolium repens*) are short-long-day plants. Our information on these plants is still quite limited. Long-day and short-day requirements of the long-short-day plants do not seem to differ fundamentally from those of the long- and the short-day plants, respectively. In most if not all short-long-day plants which have been described so far the short-day requirement can also be satisfied by low temperatures, and we do not know whether it is identical with the short-day response in short-day plants. The existence of two opposite photoperiod responses in one and the same plant has considerable fundamental interest, but because of our lack of adequate experimental data —and lack of time—I will not try to discuss the point.

I should mention that cold and daylength requirements, too, can be present in one and the same plant. In fact, very many cold-requiring plants —like the cold-requiring *Hyoscyamus* strains or most of the winter cereals— are at the same time long-day plants, and the two requirements must again be satisfied in the right order—cold first, long-day second. One may say that the cold treatment sensitizes these plants to daylength.

The Flower Hormones

Basic evidence. After having laid the groundwork for a discussion of the physiology of flower initiation, let us now proceed to the heart of the matter. The first major advance in the area was the discovery that exposure to inductive conditions results in the appearance of messengers within the

plant which instruct the plant to proceed to flower formation. This holds equally for cold-requiring plants, for short-day plants, and for long-day and long-short-day plants.

While there are several lines of evidence, the main (and earliest) information was derived from grafting experiments. In all four response types, grafting of an induced plant onto a noninduced one causes the latter to initiate flowers. In several instances it was shown that this response occurs not only in grafts between individuals of one and the same species but also in grafts between different species and even species of different genera. It has been concluded that flower initiation is determined by *flower hormones* which are formed as a result of inductive treatments; are usually not species-specific; and can move both within a plant and across graft unions into other plants.

The first experiments were done approximately 25 years ago and, as it sometimes happens in such cases, by several investigators simultaneously, independently of each other, in different plants, but with identical results.

A few examples of flower transmission in grafting experiments are given in Figures 3-5. Figure 3 (left part) shows a noninduced *Hyoscyamus* plant of the cold-requiring variety (left-hand individual) which has formed flowers after being grafted together with an induced plant (right-hand individual). On the right side of the figure, two noninduced plants are shown, also joined in a graft. In this case, no flowering has occurred, proving that the grafting procedure as such is not responsible for the effect. Figure 4 shows the same kind of experiment with the non-cold-requiring, long-day variety of *Hyoscyamus;* the larger plant has been subjected to long days, the smaller one maintained on short

Figure 3. On the left, a noninduced cold-requiring *Hyoscyamus* plant which has been grafted together with an induced plant; on the right, two noninduced plants joined in a graft (Melchers and Lang, 1946).

Figure 4. A grafting experiment with the non-cold-requiring, long-day variety of *Hyoscyamus* (Lang, unpublished work).

days; the latter flowered under the influence of the grafting partner.

In Figure 5, we see the same kind of experiment with a short-day plant, *Perilla*. In this case, a single leaf from an induced plant has been grafted onto a noninduced one and has caused the latter to form flowers on lateral shoots.

Figure 5. A grafting experiment with the short-day plant, *Perilla* (Courtesy of Dr. J. A. D. Zeevaart).

For those of you not familiar with this type of work, Figure 6 shows how such experiments can be conducted. We see a series of tobacco plants; one shoot is kept in the open greenhouse and supplied with supplementary light, the other is maintained in a framework which can be covered, every night, with black cloth, so that these shoots receive short-day conditions. It can be clearly seen that short-day treatment of one shoot has resulted in flower formation in the long-day shoot.[1] You may object that no flowers

Figure 6. A series of Maryland Mammoth tobacco plants showing how different parts of a plant can be subjected to different photoperiods (Lang, unpublished work).

can be seen on the short-day-treated shoot, but this is for a simple reason— they have been cut off. In many cases this is a necessary procedure for getting a good transmission of the flowering response. We assume that if flowers are permitted to form on the in-

---

[1] This particular experiment did not involve any grafting, but the technique, with various modifications, can be easily adapted to grafting experiments.

duced shoot or the induced grafting partner, most of the flowering hormone is consumed in this process, little or none being left to pass across the graft union to the other partner.

Attempts at isolation of the hormones. Once solid physiological evidence for the existence of flower hormones was established, the next logical question was concerning the chemical nature of the hormone(s). However, while simple to ask, this question proved extremely difficult to answer. The first step in any work of this kind is to extract the hormone from the organism and to apply the extracts to a test organism—in this case to a noninduced plant—in order to obtain the characteristic response—in our case, to bring the plant to flower. Many investigators made such experiments; however, for a long time their efforts were quite unsuccessful. Only quite recently it was announced by a group of workers at Long Beach State College, R. G. Lincoln, D. L. Mayfield, and A. Cunningham, that they have succeeded, by means of cold methanol extraction, in obtaining an extract from flowering cocklebur plants which, when applied to noninduced cockleburs, caused a significant flowering response. This looks indeed much like the first successful extraction of a flower hormone; however, the work is not sufficiently advanced to reveal something about the chemical nature of the material, and whether it is active only in the cocklebur or—as one should expect—also in other plants.

Relation of the hormones of different response types. We have seen that there is evidence for flower hormones in cold-requiring plants, in long-day plants, and in short-day plants, and that these hormones are not species-specific. An obvious question then is, are the flower hormones of these different response types identical or not? For a definite answer we will have to wait until the hormones have been extracted and identified. However, a good deal of information has been gained by physiological approaches, namely, by further grafting experiments.

First, let us examine experiments concerning the relation of the flower hormones of a photoperiodically sensitive plant—in this case a short-day plant—and a cold-requiring plant. Figure 7 is a diagrammatic representation of grafts of Maryland Mammoth tobacco onto noninduced *Hyoscyamus* plants of the cold-requiring variety. If the Maryland Mammoth was subjected to short days and was therefore in the flowering condition, it caused flower initiation in *Hyoscyamus* quite readily (left), an effect which is not too surprising. But if the Maryland Mammoth partner was maintained on long days and thus stayed vegetative, it nevertheless was effective in inducing flower initiation in the non-cold-treated *Hyoscyamus* (right). In the reciprocal experiment (Figure 8) the situation is different. We obtain flowering of the Maryland Mammoth only if the *Hyoscyamus* partner had been exposed to cold (left) but not if it had been left uninduced (right).

Thus, we seem to be faced with a puzzling situation. In one case, the combination of two plants, neither of which can flower by itself, results in flower formation in one of the partners; in the reverse case it does not.

Figure 7 (Left).   A diagrammatic representation of grafts of Maryland Mammoth tobacco onto noninduced *Hyoscyamus* plants of the cold-requiring variety (Melchers and Lang, 1946).

Figure 8 (Right).   A reciprocal experiment with the same varieties used in the experiment shown in Figure 7 (Melchers and Lang, 1946).

We can, however, explain these results by assuming that there are two different flowering hormones. These hormones have, in fact, been given names — vernalin and florigen — and, while this is somewhat like baptizing unborn children, we shall continue using these terms for the sake of convenience. We can then say that vernalin is formed in cold-requiring plants only after (or during) a cold treatment while in non-cold-requiring plants like Maryland Mammoth tobacco it is formed anytime, i.e., without cold. Florigen is formed in short-day plants only under short-day conditions, but *only if vernalin is present*. Vernalin is thus the physiological (although not necessarily the chemical) precursor of florigen.

Let us now examine how the long-day plants may fit into this scheme. Figure 9 shows grafts between Maryland Mammoth tobacco and the long-day species *Nicotiana sylvestris*. If the *sylvestris* partner is subjected to long days and is thus capable of flowering—no flowers can be seen because they have again been removed—it causes flowering in the short-day partner (right). But if the long-day partner is kept in short-day conditions, there is no such effect (left).

Figure 9. Grafts between Maryland Mammoth tobacco and the long-day species *Nicotiana sylvestris* (A. K. Khudairi and A. Lang, unpublished work).

In the reciprocal experiment (Figures 10 and 11—Maryland Mammoth tobacco was again used as the short-day partner but non-cold-requiring *Hyoscyamus* as the long-day partner), if the short-day plant is kept in long days and the long-day plant in short days, there is no flowering (Figure 10), but if the former is kept in short days and can flower (Figure 11—the flowers have been removed), then it does cause flowering in the long-day partner. Thus, if we graft together long- and short-day plants, flowering occurs only if one of the partners is given inductive conditions. The conclusion is that the flower hormones of long- and short-day plants are identical, so that we have altogether two flower hormones and can write their relation in the following way:

——————————————→ Vernalin ——————————————→ Florigen — — — — —→ Flower formation

Cold-requiring plants: Long-day plants:
with cold-treatment only   *in long-day only*
Non-cold-requiring plants: Short-day plants:
without cold   *in short-day only*

Figure 10 (left) and Figure 11 (right). Grafts between Maryland Mammoth as the short-day partner and non-cold-requiring *Hyoscyamus* as the long-day partner (Khudairi and Lang, unpublished work).

Formation and translocation of the hormones. In addition to our insight into the relation of the flower hormones of cold-requiring and photoperiodic plants, we possess substantial insight into the sites of their formation and into the translocation of florigen.

Localized chilling experiments and other approaches have shown that it is sufficient to cold-treat the growing region of cold-requiring plants in order to secure flower formation. Vernalin thus seems to be produced in the shoot meristems and/or the youngest, not-yet-expanded leaves, although this does not rule out that it may also be formed in older leaves.

Florigen, in contrast, is formed in relatively older, expanded leaves. This has been shown in two different ways: (1) Long- and short-day plants flower if only the leaves are subjected to inductive photoperiods, while the growing points—the sites of the response—are maintained on noninductive conditions; the inverse treatment does not result in flower formation. (2) If a plant is induced but the leaves removed immediately after induction no flower formation occurs. (This experiment is best done with plants responding to a single inductive cycle.) By treating individual leaves of different age, it was shown that the half-grown to the youngest fully grown leaf is usually the most sensitive one, i.e., its treatment results in the highest flowering response.

The first leaves of some plants never seem to reach a high degree of "sensitivity" and grafting experiments have proved that they never produce substantial amounts of florigen. This is at least one of the reasons why many plants cannot flower, even under optimal inductive photoperiods, before having passed through a certain period of vegetative growth. Other plants, however, can form large amounts of florigen even in their cotyledons.

Since vernalin is formed so close to its site of action, little is known about its translocation. In the case of florigen we know that it moves only in living tissue; we know how long it takes to move out of an induced leaf; and we have good estimates of its translocation rate.

The need of living tissue was demonstrated by girdling experiments. The girdles can be made mechanically, i.e., by removing certain tissues (e.g., the stem cortex); by means of steam jets; or by means of narcotics. They all result in suppression of florigen movement. It is very probable that the movement occurs in the phloem.

The time of movement from the leaf was determined by removing leaves at different times after the end of inductive treatment. It was shown that this time in *Xanthium* is 12-24 hours while in *Pharbitis* it is markedly shorter, only 4-5 hours.

Translocation rates were determined from the distances which had to be traversed, and the time needed for the first visible response. The values are in the order of 5-10 cm. per day. This is considerably below the rate for photosynthates, so that it is not certain whether florigen travels by a simple mass movement.

"Persistence" of hormone formation. Some photoperiodically sensitive plants, once induced, persist in the flowering state for extended periods of time, some for the rest of their lives.

Moreover, grafting experiments have shown that one such plant (or part of it) can "infect" a whole series of non-induced plants. Two cases must be distinguished in this respect:

(1) In *Perilla,* it is necessary to use a leaf that has been directly exposed to short days, but one such leaf, grafted onto 4-5 different, noninduced plants, on one after the other, caused all these plants to flower. The degree of response showed no decline; the experiments were terminated only by the death of the leaf. Leaves (or other plant parts) which had not been given a direct short-day exposure were not able to evoke any flowering response, even if they came from flowering plants.

(2) In *Xanthium,* it was possible to graft an induced plant onto a noninduced one, then graft the latter onto a second noninduced plant, and so forth, and in this manner to serially induce at least four plants.

In either case, it is unlikely that these results can be explained by formation of a finite, albeit large amount of florigen in the first leaf or first plant; it rather seems that florigen, once its production has started, continues to be formed indefinitely—in *Perilla* in the photoinduced leaves, in *Xanthium* in the flowering plant as a whole (apparently in the young, growing parts) even if this plant was never directly exposed to short days.

The first thought that comes to one's mind is that florigen itself is self-perpetuating, that it has the nature of a virus. But some experimental evidence, into which it would take too much time to go in detail, suggests that florigen is, on the contrary, rather short-lived. It is therefore not probable that florigen continues to reproduce itself, but that the *florigen-producing machinery,* once it has started functioning, may continue to function for indefinite periods of time. This is a situation for which we have few if any precise counterparts in other, normal living systems and which is, therefore, one of the most intriguing aspects of flowering physiology and one which will undoubtedly attract much further attention.

The Phytochrome System

Let us now return to the flower hormones as such. We have seen that low temperature and photoperiod control the formation of different flower hormones (vernalin and florigen, respectively) so that we can explain the difference between low-temperature-requiring and daylength-dependent plants in these simple terms. But what about long- and short-day plants? They seem to possess the same hormone; but they form the hormone under opposite day-length conditions. Thus, they must in some manner differ in the events which lead to hormone formation; specifically, there must be at least one point at which they exhibit opposite responses to daylength.

Can we identify this pivotal point? Whenever we are dealing with a phenomenon that depends on light, we must assume the presence of a pigment which absorbs the light energy. It is thus obviously of the greatest significance to know what pigments perform this initial act in photoperiodism; are these pigments perhaps that point which is different in long- and short-day plants?

The first step towards identification of a physiologically active pigment is to determine its action spectrum, that is, to determine which wavelengths are effective in producing the particular response. When determined critically and interpreted judiciously, the action spectrum reflects the absorption spectrum of the pigment; this serves as one of the main characteristics of the pigment and as a guide in its isolation and purification—in some cases it can in fact give a good indication of its chemical nature.

In actual work, much depends on a simple, effective system for the determination of an action spectrum. In the case of the "photoperiodic" pigment, such a system was provided by the so-called light-flash technique.

If we expose a plant to cycles of 8 hours of light and 16 hours of darkness, we will of course obtain the short-day response; a short-day plant will flower, a long-day plant stay vegetative. However, in order to get a long-day response we need not give the plant full 16 hours of natural daylight or other high-intensity illumination. We can give 8 hours of high-intensity light, and extend this period with 8 hours of light of quite a low intensity. To give you an approximate idea, I may mention that the light of the full moon has a significant photoperiodic effect in some plants.

But we can do even better. We can give an 8-hour day with a 16-hour dark period, but interrupt the latter with a so-called light flash, i.e., a short period of light. If this is done in the middle of the dark period, we get a long-day

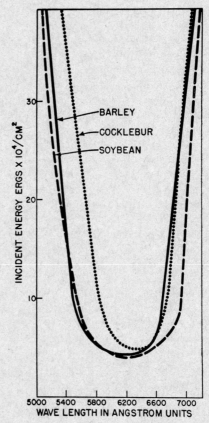

Figure 12. The photoperiodic action spectrum of long- and short-day plants (Borthwick, 1959).

effect as with cycles consisting of 16 hours of light and 8 hours of dark. Again, we need but relatively little light energy to accomplish this effect.

These experiments provide us with a handy system for determining the kind of light that is active in the photoperiodic control of flower formation. Such work was done in a most elegant and efficient fashion by a group of workers at the USDA Plant Industry Station at Beltsville, Md., headed by H. A. Borthwick and S. B. Hendricks. Figure 12 shows the action spectrum which they established for several plants. The curve is a plot of the incident energy which is necessary to produce a certain effect, against wavelength; thus, whenever the curve approaches the abscissa, we are in a region of high effectiveness. We see that the major effectiveness is in the red region of about 6,200-6,400 A; a second, much weaker region of effectiveness (not shown in the figure) can be found in the blue. A particularly important point is that the curves for short-day plants (soybean, cocklebur) and long-day plants (barley) are very similar, suggesting that the light perception in either plant type is mediated by the same pigment.

The "photoperiodic pigment" possesses another remarkable and important characteristic which has also been demonstrated by the Beltsville team. If the dark period is interrupted with red light, we obtain the long-day response. But if immediately after giving the red interruption we expose the plant to light of a wavelength about 7,200-7,400 A, so-called far-red light, we obtain the short-day response. This can be repeated several times, back and forth; when the last irradiation is with red, we have the long-day response, when it is with far-red, the short-day response, although the far-red reversibility may become increasingly smaller with each reversal.

Flowering of Cocklebur as Controlled by Red and Far-Red Interruption of the Dark Period

(After Borthwick, 1959)

Interruption[1]	Response[2]
None	6.0
R	0
R-FR	5.6
R-FR-R	0
R-FR-R-FR	4.2
R-FR-R-FR-R	0
R-FR-R-FR-R-FR	2.4
R-FR-R-FR-R-FR-R	0
R-FR-R-FR-R-FR-R-FR	0.6

[1] R = red, FR = far red.

[2] 0— Vegetative; 1, 2 . . . — Increasing flowering response.

In other systems the reversibility is complete, so that we get each time exactly the same response levels for red and for far-red.

On the basis of these results it was concluded that we are dealing with a pigment which exists in two interconvertible forms. One form absorbs in the red and, by the energy absorbed, is converted into the second form. This absorbs in the far-red and by the light energy absorbed is reconverted into the first form; and this back-and-forth conversion can be repeated again and again. It was further shown that conversion from the far-red- to the red-absorbing form also occurs in the dark, although slowly. We can accordingly formulate the relation of the two pigment forms as follows:

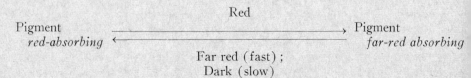

Pigment *red-absorbing*   Red → Pigment *far-red absorbing* ← Far red (fast); Dark (slow)

On the basis of this information we can now interpret what happens during a long dark period. Because the pigment's relative sensitivity to red is greater than to far-red, the pigment at the end of the daily light period is predominantly in the far-red-absorbing form. In the course of the dark period it slowly changes to the red-absorbing form. Extension with light, even of low intensity, prevents this change; brief irradiation with white or red light throws the pigment back into the far-red absorbing form.

In the last five years, the Beltsville workers have succeeded in extracting the pigment from dark-grown seedlings of maize and other plants; in accomplishing a high degree of purification; and in pushing it back and forth between the two forms *in vitro* just as it had been possible within the plant. The pigment has been called *phytochrome*. It is a protein carrying a chromophoric group and is very likely an enzyme, although at present nothing can yet be said about the chemical nature of the chromophoric group or the enzymatic function of the pigment. Phytochrome has been shown to be involved in the regulation of numerous other plant responses, for example seed germination, stem and leaf growth, and anthocyanin formation in seedlings. It seems to be a central system in the utilization of light energy for the control of plant function.

Kinetics of the Photoperiodic Responses of Long- and Short-Day Plants

The discovery and analysis of phytochrome and its operation is one of the most fascinating stories in plant physiology. But does it solve the riddle of photoperiodism? For the time being no; if anything, the riddle may appear tougher than ever. As we have seen, the last part of the photoperiodic mechanism, the flower hormone, is identical in long- and short-day plants. Now, we find that the light-absorbing system is also identical.

Phytochrome is thus not the point at which the photoperiodic mechanisms of long- and short-day plants differ. At present, we do not know what this pivotal point is; all we can do is to indicate how plant biologists are trying to search for it.

One line of approach consists of resolving the events which occur during photoinduction into a series of individual, well-defined steps or "partial processes." The rationale is that in this way we can study relatively simpler systems, one at a time, and will ultimately bridge the gap between the light absorption by phytochrome and the synthesis of florigen, and in this process may also recognize the point at which long- and short-day plants exhibit a difference in their photoperiodic machineries.

Let us retrace our steps to the very beginning of our discussion, the exposition of the two main photoperiodic response types, forgetting, for the moment, even the existence of flower hormones. Then the flowering response of long-day and short-day plants can be interpreted in two alternative ways. We can assume that, with regard to flower formation, inductive conditions have a positive, promotive action or that noninductive conditions have an inhibitory one. It appears that either alternative may exist in either response type.

In a long-day plant like *Hyoscyamus* (non-cold-requiring strain), any measure which reduces the length or effectiveness of a long dark period (low-intensity light; light interruption in the middle; low temperature during the dark period) results in flower formation, suggesting that long dark periods are the crucial factor and that they somehow actively inhibit flower formation. This conclusion is supported by direct evidence. Defoliation of a *Hyoscyamus* plant makes it capable of forming flowers not only in long days, but also in short days and even in continuous light.

Figure 13 shows a defoliated *Hyoscyamus* plant with a well-developed flower (usually, however, the flowers do not reach such a stage). The inhibitory action of long dark periods apparently resides in the leaves of *Hyoscyamus;* removal of the leaves removes the plant from photoperiodic control.

In another long-day plant, *Lolium temulentum,* it was however found that, while long dark periods also exert an inhibitory action, the light periods have a clear promotive effect.

In short-day plants, the situation is similar, but with the opposite sign. In some cases (*Xanthium, Pharbitis*) it appears that the photoperiod response is entirely based on some flower-promoting events occurring in long dark

Figure 13. A defoliated *Hyoscyamus* plant with a well-developed flower (Melchers, unpublished work).

periods. In others (*Kalanchoe,* soybean, *Perilla*), we have conclusive evidence of an inhibitory action of long light periods; long dark periods are needed for the removal of this inhibition, although they seem to have a positive action as well. These findings do not explain the opposite behavior of long- and short-day plants towards daylength. However, they suggest that different plants can accomplish photoperiodic control of flowering in somewhat different manners; we may thus have to seek for more than a single difference.

Returning to the flower-hormone concept, there is little reason to doubt that the "positive effect" of inductive photoperiods of which we have been speaking is the production of florigen.

As to the "inhibitory effects," we know very little. Some authors postulate inhibitory substances acting as "anti-florigens," but this hypothesis is based on little conclusive evidence. It rather seems that the inhibitory effects are not transmissible. The existence of inhibitors, perhaps formed under the action of the "wrong" phytochrome form, is not ruled out, but if present they seem to remain in the leaves where they are formed, and to concern the production of florigen, not its action.

Effects of Chemical Substances on Photoperiodic Induction

Metabolites and anti-metabolites. Another approach to finding out more about the mechanism of photoperiodism and to finding the reason for the different behavior of long- and short-day plants, has been the use of certain chemical materials. The basic idea is to modify the flowering response of the plant by applying chemicals or other treatments which modify metabolism in a known manner, and thus to obtain insights into the metabolic events which take place during photoperiodic induction. This type of approach is particularly efficient in plants which can be induced by a single inductive photoperiod, since this avoids the complications inherent in repetitive treatments and permits pinpointing effects of applied materials or treatments to particular phases of the inductive cycle, such as the light period or particular times of the dark period.

By use of this approach, some very interesting results have been obtained. In long-day plants, it was found that flower formation can be obtained under noninductive conditions by such simple measures as sugar feeding and anaerobic conditions (nitrogen atmosphere).

In short-day plants, the effect of inductive conditions could be suppressed by respiratory poisons and by inhibitors of nucleic acid synthesis. The effect of respiratory poisons shows that the inductive processes depend on respiratory energy, but does not reveal anything about the nature of these processes. The effect of antagonists of nucleic acid synthesis indicates that this latter process is essential for effective induction. However, this effect is localized in the buds, not in the leaves, and is thus related not to florigen production but to florigen function and flower differentiation. From these viewpoints, this work may become very interesting but it does not yield specific information on the nature of the photoinductive processes, nor on their differences in long- and short-day plants.

Effects of plant growth substances on photoperiodic induction. Chemical substances of another type which have been used in the study of photoperiodic control of flower formation are certain plant growth regulators or plant growth hormones. The rationale behind their use is briefly as follows: In contrast to most animal hormones, plant hormones are not particularly specific in their action. We know now of three major groups of native or endogenous growth hormones in higher plants, the auxins, gibberellins, and kinins. However, we cannot assign to any one of them a single, dis-

Figure 14. A cold-requiring plant (the carrot)—untreated (left), gibberellin-treated (center), cold-treated (right) (Lang, 1957).

tinctive major function. They rather seem all to be involved in the regulation of very many different plant growth processes, and how the plant is growing may depend on their ratios rather than their absolute levels. It therefore seemed interesting to check whether these plant growth hormones also have an effect on flowering.

Kinetin has been shown to promote flower formation in noninduced or incompletely induced short-day plants, but it is dubious whether the effect is directly concerned with photoinduction.

Auxin counteracts the effect of inductive conditions in short-day plants and may, in rather particular circumstances, enhance it in long-day plants. This is basically very interesting, for it seems to qualify auxin for the pivotal point of difference between the two response types; one might think it inhibits flower formation in short-day plants and promotes it in long-day plants. Unfortunately, the situation is complicated by certain other results, and—the most important drawback— auxin effects on photoinduction are generally too small to account for the full effect of inductive (or noninductive) photoperiod conditions.

The situation is different in the case of the gibberellins. Treatment with these compounds can completely or partially "replace" inductive conditions in cold-requiring and long-day plants. This is illustrated by the following two figures. Figure 14 shows a cold-requiring plant, the carrot: at the left, a non-cold-treated plant; at the right one that received 6 weeks of cold and then was returned to the greenhouse; in the middle one that stayed in the greenhouse, but received daily gibberellin applications. It is clear that the latter treatment has produced the same flowering response as the "natural" (cold) treatment.

Figure 15 shows the response of a long-day plant, *Samolus parviflorus*

Figure 15. The response of a long-day plant *(Samolus parviflorus)* to treatment with gibberellin (Lang, 1957).

(water pimpernel). All plants were kept on short days; the left group shows controls which have stayed vegetative; progressing to the right the plants were treated with increasing amounts of gibberellin and gave an increasing flowering response. Other work has shown that inductive treatment of cold-requiring and long-day plants is associated with profound changes in the gibberellin content of the plants. Thus it is likely that gibberellins perform some function related to flower formation, but what function is it? Are gibberellins the flower hormones, or can they be the differentiating point between long- and short-day plants?

Neither interpretation is probable. We have seen that the flower hormones which are controlled by cold and by daylength are different. But gibberellens can substitute for cold and long-day requirements; they do not seem capable of inducing flower formation in short-day plants kept under strictly noninductive conditions, i.e., of substituting for short-day requirements. Thus, they fit neither the part of florigen, nor that of the factor toward which long- and short-day plants show opposite behavior. The gibberellins may be needed for flower-hormone formation and in cold-requiring and long-day plants may be a limiting factor of this process, but their precise role in flower formation is not yet understood. Some evidence which cannot be discussed here in detail suggests that they may be primarily involved in stem elongation, and that this in some unexplained way is a prerequisite for flower formation. If this is so, the effect of gibberellins on flowering would be an indirect one.

Endogenous Rhythms and Photoperiodic Induction of Flower Formation

I am approaching the end of my talk—the point when the speaker is expected to integrate the information he has presented and fuse it into a simple and persuasive, all-illuminating picture. I shall proceed differently, trying to make a confused picture still more confused.

One interesting aspect of photoperiodism, although it has not been emphasized in the earlier work, is that it is a phenomenon of *time measurement*. The plant measures the length of the day and thus determines the time of the year; this information is essential to adjust its development to seasonal conditions.

It is believed by an increasing number of biologists that plants as well as animals possess so-called internal or endogenous clocks. Some biologists who have been working in this field assume that whenever a plant or an animal is measuring time it is using the built-in clock and that the photoperiodic control of flowering in plants is therefore also connected with this clock. The internal clock operates on a cycle length of approximately 24 hours, and it has been shown that there are indeed rhythmic effects in photoperiodic responses which follow a 24-hour periodicity.

The most conclusive results of this

kind have been obtained by K. C. Hamner at UCLA. An example is shown in the last illustration (Figure 16). This figure shows the response of soybean plants which received cycles all having the same light period (8 hours) but dark periods of different length. We see a nice, rhythmic response with maxima of flowering at total cycle lengths of 24, 48, and 72 hours, and minima at 36 and 60 hours. However, other work indicates that these periodic variations of the flowering response are of a quantitative nature while the photoperiodic response itself is often a qualitative one (flowering; or no flowering at all), and that they do not occur in all photoperiodic plants. It therefore seems to me that the endogenous clock is not directly involved in the photoperiodic responses, although it may modify them in a secondary manner.

There are also other reasons why the endogenous clock does not help us much in understanding photoperiodic responses. Firstly, the mechanism of

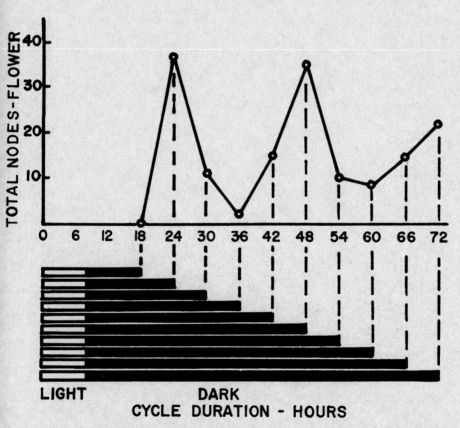

Figure 16. The response of soybean plants to cycles of light and darkness. The number of nodes carrying flowers is a measure of the flowering response in soybeans (Courtesy of Professor K. C. Hamner).

the clock is still entirely unknown. Thus, even if we accept the tenet of absolute endogenicity of the clock and assume that photoperiodic responses are indeed dependent on the latter, we do nothing to resolve them; we are merely shifting the problem to another area. Secondly, it has been shown that the endogenous clocks of long- and short-day plants operate on exactly the same phase. They thus cannot directly explain the opposite behavior of the two response types with regard to the length of day; we would still have to explain how measurements of time with one and the same clock are used to accomplish opposite responses.

Concluding Remarks

The dependence of flower formation on low temperature and on daylength was fully recognized some 40 years ago. Since that period, an enormous amount of literature has been published, but the major part has been of a descriptive nature and does not contribute to a causal understanding of the phenomena. In trying to evaluate the progress that has been made towards such an understanding, we find that, using different approaches, we have reached different levels of information. With regard to phytochrome, we are at the molecular level. The substance has been isolated and it is only a matter of time before we will know what it is and what it does. With regard to the flowering hormones, or at least florigen, we may be just across the threshold of this same level and have a considerable background of information at the level of the whole plant.

In the effect of gibberellin on flower formation, we have another instance where we can use biochemical approaches in trying to evaluate the role of specific, endogenous substances in flower formation. But there is still an area—the gap between phytochrome on the one side, florigen and possibly gibberellin on the other—where our information is deficient and of a kinetic nature; we can describe certain events in terms of promotion, inhibition, etc., but not in biophysical and biochemical terms. It is not at all certain that the gap is a very wide one; as our information on the biochemistry and biophysics of phytochrome and florigen increases it may in fact be largely bridged. But at present, as I have tried to explain, we do not understand the precise relation between those two end points of the photoperiodic sequence, particularly if we view photoperiodism in a comprehensive manner, considering long- and short-day plants alike. With regard to vernalization—about which I did not talk, except the hormonal aspects—all information we possess is of the kinetic type.

Thus, there clearly remains much work to do. But if we utilize the various leads which we already have, chances seem good that we will arrive at a comprehensive physiological picture of flower formation, and in not too long a time.

Questions and Answers

QUESTION: The relation of red to far-red in long and short days is a very interesting one. I wonder if the ratio of intensity of red and far-red light changes as the days change from short to long, and if there could be a correlation between such changes and the daylength response?

ANSWER: The ratio of red and far-red does seem to undergo variations which depend on time of day, time of year, and local climatic conditions, e.g., the amount of water vapor in the atmosphere which tends to attenuate the far-red radiation. But I was unable to find any precise data on this point and therefore cannot answer your question in any quantitative manner. However, as far as we are aware and as far as flower formation is concerned plants seem to see daylight always as red so that, as already mentioned, the phytochrome pigment at the beginning of the dark period is predominantly in the far-red-absorbing condition.

I do not believe that relative changes in the red and far-red intensity are great enough to alter this situation. I would however like to remark that I have presented the red and far-red responses in a somewhat simplified manner. The effects in the middle of the dark period are almost always as I have related. But applied for longer periods of time or at the beginning of the dark period, red and far-red sometimes seem to produce different effects.

In my opinion, it will not be possible to resolve these problems by physiological means; the best procedure is probably to wait until Dr. Hendricks and his co-workers have perfected the isolation and characterization of the pigment and then to analyze its condition in the plant throughout the photoperiodic cycle and under the influence of different irradiation schedules.

QUESTION: I would like to ask if you care to comment about the so-called fat-soluble florigens which Dr. R. H. Roberts of the University of Wisconsin has mentioned from time to time?

ANSWER: I can answer this question only in very tentative terms as no details of this work seem so far to have been published. I think, however, that it is fair to say that these materials do not cause flowering under strict noninductive conditions, but only if the plants are over the threshold of photoinduction. Under these conditions, treatment with these preparations seems to result sometimes in extremely striking increases of the flowering response. Thus, I suspect that the materials do not affect the inception of flowering, but the further development of flowers that have been initiated. In this respect, I would not call the materials genuine florigens.

QUESTION (DR. BICKOFF): In a large number of different plants we know that there are estrogens somewhat similar to animal estrogens, and we know that these estrogens vary during the lifetime of plants, often increasing during the flowering stage. What is your feeling of the possible relationship of this to the reproductive cycle of the plant itself?

ANSWER: I am once more afraid that I cannot tell you anything in conclusive terms. Attempts at applying various estrogens to plants and causing flower formation have been unsuccessful, although some quantitative growth effects have been reported in other systems. However, there are serious problems in the application of these substances—which are practically insoluble in water—to plants, and it is possible that the earlier results are not altogether conclusive.

Recently, interest in lipid compounds as possible regulatory substances has revived and more work in relation to flowering seems indicated. In this connection, I would like to ask a question in turn: Would extraction of plants with absolute methanol in the cold (as used by Lincoln, Mayfield, and Cunningham) extract estrogens and other lipid material efficiently?

DR. BICKOFF: You can extract these materials with acetone, and I suspect that you can also extract them with methanol although I haven't actually done it.

QUESTION: Would you care to speculate on the mechanism of the transmission of information from the phytochrome to the ultimate flowering response?

ANSWER: This brings us back to probably the biggest unsolved problem with which we are still faced in photoperiodism. As I have explained, the initial receptor for the information—the pigment—is the same, and so seems the ultimate messenger—florigen—; however, something must be different in long- and short-day plants between the two, and this something we just don't know. As to the possible action of phytochrome, Dr. Hendricks has suggested that it may be an enzyme involved in transfer of activated acetyl; however, I have no business sticking his neck out here.

QUESTION: Is there any difference in the response of field-grown or forest-grown plants of different ecological types grown under different conditions, or sun- and shade-plants?

ANSWER: I feel certain that the photoperiod response of plants is basically determined by phytochrome. This however needs relatively very small energies for its conversion. Therefore, I do not think the photoperiodic response will differ basically in different ecological types or in sun- and shade-plants, etc. However, the light periods of the daily cycles may also have some effect on the response. For example, some long-day plants when given long-day conditions but low light intensity may fail to flower, and so may short-day plants if the inductive long dark periods are not preceded by periods of high-intensity light. In this respect, I expect different plants may differ. However, these effects do not seem specific for flowering. It seems that the plant has to have a sufficient supply of photosynthate before it can afford such a luxury as sex.

To give you an idea of the light energies which suffice to obtain typical phytochrome responses, let me give you the following figures: The sunlight on a clear day has an intensity of 10^5 microwatts per square centimeter. Full moonlight has 2×10^{-2} $\mu W/cm^2$; this—as I mentioned—is sufficient for photoperiodic flower induction. The threshold at which one can observe photoperiodic flower induction in the most sensitive plants is about 10^{-2} μW. Other phytochrome-dependent systems are still much more sensitive; for the growth of the first internode of a dark-grown oat or bean plant the threshold value is 10^{-8} μW/cm.^{2}, a truly amazing value. It means approximately 3 x 10^4 quanta per square centimeter per second and, if one assumes that the surface of a single cell is roughly 0.1 by 0.1 millimeters, 3 quanta per cell per second. To give you for comparison data for human vision, the threshold for cone or color vision is at 10^{-2} to 10^{-3} μW/cm.^{2}, i.e., close to that in photoperiodic control of flowering; for rod vision in the dark-adapted eye is about 10^{-5} μW/cm.^{2} Thus, the dark-grown plant has a "vision" still 1,000 times better than ours.

REFERENCES

General review articles

P. Chouard, 1960. Vernalization and its relation to dormancy. Ann. Rev. Plant Physiol., *11:* 191-238.

J. Doorenbos, and S. J. Wellensiek, 1959. Photoperiodic control of flower induction. Ann. Rev. Plant Physiol., *10:*147-148.

A. Lang, 1952. Physiology of flowering. Ann. Rev. Plant Physiol., *3:*265-306.

A. Lang. "Physiology of flower initiation." In *Encyclopedia of Plant Physiology*. W. Ruhland, ed., *15.* (In press.)

J. A. Lockhart, 1961. Mechanism of the photoperiodic process in higher plants. In *Encyclopedia of Plant Physiology,* W. Ruhland, ed., *16:*390-438.

G. Melchers, and A. Lang, 1948. Physiologie der Blütenbildung. Biol. Zentralbl., *67:*105-174.

A. W. Naylor, 1961. "The photoperiodic control of plant behavior." In *Encyclopedia of Plant Physiology.* W. Ruhland, ed., *16:*331-389.

O. N. Purvis, 1961. "The physiological analysis of vernalization." In *Encyclopedia of Plant Physiology.* W. Ruhland, ed., *16:*76-122.

F. B. Salisbury, 1961. Photoperiodism and the flowering process. Ann. Rev. Plant Physiol., *12:*293-326.

Selected references on individual problems

1) Flower hormones

S. Imamura, and A. Takimoto, 1955. Transmission rate of photoperiodic stimulus in *Pharbitis nil.* Bot. Mag. (Tokyo), *68:*260-266.

A. K. Khudairi, and K. C. Hamner, 1954. The relative sensitivity of *Xanthium* leaves of different ages to photoperiodic induction. Plant Physiol., *29:*251-257.

G. Melchers, and A. Lang, 1948. (See general review articles.)

R. G. Lincoln, D. L. Mayfield, and A. Cunningham, 1961. Preparation of a floral initiating extract from *Xanthium.* Science, *133:*756.

J. A. D. Zeevaart, 1958. Flower formation as studied by grafting. Meded. Landbouwhogesch. Wageningen, *58,* No. 3.

2) Phytochrome

H. A. Borthwick, 1959. "Photoperiodic control of flowering." In *Photoperiodism and Related Phenomena in Plants and Animals,* R. B. Withrow, ed. AAAS Publ. No. 55, pp. 75-87.

H. A. Borthwick and S. B. Hendricks, 1960. Photoperiodism in plants. Science, *132:*1223-1228.

W. L. Butler, K. H. Norris, H. W. Siegelman, and S. B. Hendricks, 1959. Detection, assay, and preliminary purification of the pigment controlling photo-responsive development in plants. Proc. Nat. Acad. Sci., *45:*1703-1708.

3) Kinetics

J. Bonner, 1959. "The photoperiodic process." In *Photoperiodism and Related Phenomena in Plants and Animals,* R. B. Withrow, ed. AAAS Publ. No. 55, pp. 245-254.

L. T. Evans, 1960. Inflorescence initiation in *Lolium temulentum.* II. Evidence for inhibitory and promotive photoperiodic processes involving transmissible products. Austral. Jour. Biol. Sci., *13:*429-440.

A. Lang and G. Melchers, 1943. Die photoperiodische Reaktion von *Hyoscyamus niger.* Planta, *33:*657-702.

W. W. Schwabe, 1959. "Recent work on the inhibitory effect of long days on the flowering of some short-day plants." In *Colloque International sur le Thermo-Photoperiodism.* Publ. Internat. Union Biol. Sci., Ser. B, No. 34, pp. 95-109.

4) Effects of chemical substances

M. Kh. Chailakhyan, 1961. "Effect of gibberellins and derivatives of nuclei acid metabolism on plant growth and flowering." In *Plant Growth Regulation.* Ames, Iowa State Univ. Press, pp. 531-542.

A. Lang, 1958. Induction of reproductive growth in plants. Proc. 4th Internat. Congr. Bioch., *6:*129-139.

A. Lang, 1959. "Influence of gibberellin and auxin on photoperiodic induction." In *Photoperiodism and Related Phenomena in Plants and Animals,* R. B. Withrow, ed. AAAS Publ. No. 55, pp. 329-350.

A. Lang, and E. Reinhard, 1961. Gibberellins and flower formation. Adv. in Chem., *28:*71-79.

F. B. Salisbury, and J. Bonner, 1960. Inhibition of photoperiodic induction by 5-fluorouracil. Plant Physiol., *35:*173-177.

5) Endogenous rhythms

E. Bünning, 1960. Circadian rhythms and the time measurement in photoperiodism. Cold Spring Harbor Symp., *25:*248-256.

K. C. Hamner, 1960. Photoperiodism and circadian rhythms. Cold Spring Harbor Symp., *25:*269-277.

Evidence for the Hormonal Control of Sexual Reproduction in *Oedogonium* and *Allomyces*

LEONARD MACHLIS[1]

Botany Department
University of California, Berkeley

I F TIME permitted, extensive evidence could be presented that sexual reproduction in plants is controlled and integrated by hormones (Raper, 1952, 1954, 1957, 1960; Naf, 1948, 1960; Jaffe, 1958; Rothschild, 1956; and the article, "The Physiology of Reproduction in Higher Plants," by Dr. Anton Lang in this publication). None of these hormones has been fully characterized chemically. About four years ago I initiated work with the objective of identifying certain sexual hormones functioning in algae and fungi. The many technical details and background literature, omitted because of lack of time, are available in papers already published (Machlis, 1958a, 1959b) or will be made available in future publications.

I will first discuss the filamentous watermold *Allomyces*. The vegetative body of this fungus consists of the usual web of cotton-like threads. On a nutrient agar plate the mycelium quickly covers the surface and appears bright orange because of the presence of numerous gametangia. These are of two types: small, orange male gametangia and large, colorless female gametangia, borne in terminal pairs (Figure 1). When scraped from the agar surface and placed in water, these gametangia release in an hour or two, motile male and female gametes. Male gametes can be observed clustering around undischarged female gametangia, thus becoming willing prey for female gametes which will soon emerge.

[1] The unpublished research discussed has been supported by research grants NSF-G-7031 and NSF-G-13167 from the National Science Foundation and by a research professorship in the Adolph C. and Mary Sprague Miller Institute for Basic Research in Science of the University of California at Berkeley.

GAMETES

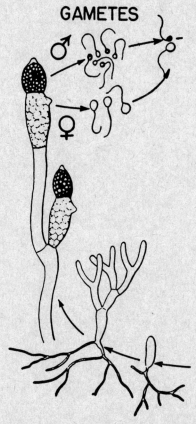

Figure 1. Diagramatic representation of the mycelium, gametangia, and gametes of *Allomyces*. The male gametangia and gametes are bright orange. Part of a drawing made by Rafael Rodriguez and reproduced by permission of Arthur T. Brice.

This simple observation and several months of corroborating experiments led to the conclusion that female gametes secrete a chemical lure by which male gametes can locate them; and to the decision to learn the nature of the lure which was subsequently named sirenin.

The first requisite was a bioassay. In this endeavor nature was generous.

Unisexual plants were obviously desirable for both the production of sirenin and for a bioassay. My colleague, Professor Ralph Emerson, together with Dr. Charles Wilson (1954) had earlier observed that some of the progeny of crosses between certain species of *Allomyces* often had ratios of male to female gametangia deviating markedly from the normal 1:1 ratio. Beginning with such progeny and subjecting them to a variety of crosses, I eventually obtained several stable isolates which were 96 to 99% male or female.

When the female plants are grown in rich nutrient broth, a copious vegetative development occurs. When these plants are placed in a shallow layer of tap water with changes of the water every 8 hours, female gametes are produced in large numbers for about 3 days; simultaneously, sirenin is secreted into the water.

The male plants can be grown on squares of filter paper giving dense, red colonies as shown in Figure 2.

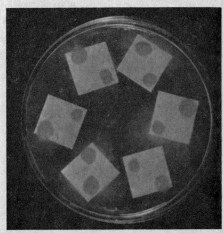

Figure 2. Growth of male *Allomyces* plants on filter paper layered over nutrient agar. The plants are bright orange.

Two hours after immersing these papers bearing the plants in water, a suspension of sperm containing up to 1.1×10^6 sperm per ml. is ready for use in the bioassay. The apparatus used for the assay is shown in Figures 3 and 4. It consists of two perforated stainless steel plates between which a sheet of dialyzing membrane is tightly held with the aid of a rubber gasket. The lower part of the assembled apparatus is immersed in the sperm suspension and is supported by the heads of the six clamping bolts. Test solutions are placed in the holes above the membrane. After approximately 40 minutes sperm are attached to the under surface of the membrane in proportion to the concentration of

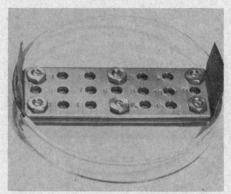

Figure 4. The assembled bioassay apparatus in place in the petri dish (standard 100 x 15 mm.).

sirenin above the membrane; these are readily counted under the microscope (Figures 5 and 6).

With this assay it was established that sirenin can be chromatographed on silicic acid-impregnated paper and partially purified using a silicic acid column. At this time in late 1959 a decision was made to attempt a large-scale production of sirenin and Professor Henry Rapoport of the Department of Chemistry at Berkeley agreed to attempt to work out final purification procedures and the structural chemistry. Although we have now been producing sirenin for some 15 months and the chemical work has proceeded vigorously, we are unable to say anything very definite about the chemical nature of sirenin. I will take a few minutes, however, to describe briefly the production process.

Plates of female plants (Figure 7) are fragmented in a blender to provide inoculum for 14 agitated submerged flask cultures (Figure 8). The plants in each flask are again fragmented and poured into 15 liters of broth contained in 5 gallon carboys. These are grown for 3 days at 25° C.

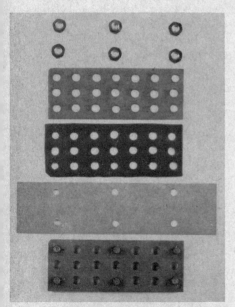

Figure 3. The unassembled bioassay apparatus. From bottom to top: the lower plate threaded with six bolts; the membrane (cardboard substituted here for visibility); the rubber gasket; the upper steel plate; and the nuts for locking the apparatus together.

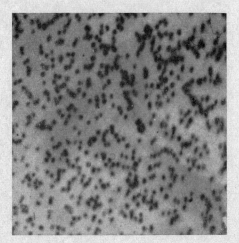

Figure 5. Sperm attached to membrane in response to sirenin. In the absence of sirenin no sperm are attached.

with aeration which also provides mechanical agitation (Figure 9). The plants are then washed thoroughly and spread in trays (Figure 10) in a shallow layer of tap water.

Every 8 hours about 3 liters of water automatically enters the trays at the rear and overflows through the tubes at the front. The overflow water —about 30 liters every 8 hours—runs down the drains, through a cloth strainer, into a plastic reservoir, and then by suction into the large tank shown in Figure 11. This sirenin- and

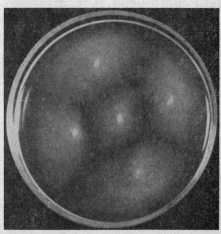

Figure 7. Plates of female plants used to begin the production cycle.

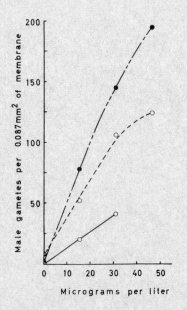

Figure 6. Representative standard curves for the bioassay of sirenin.

Figure 8. Agitated submerged cultures of female plants which will serve as inoculum for carboys.

gamete-containing water automatically
enters the low-temperature evaporator
shown in Figure 12 where it is concentrated approximately 100 times before the concentrated sample is withdrawn and frozen.

Every 2 weeks the accumulated 10
liters of concentrate is thawed, filtered,
and then extracted with chloroform for

Figure 11. Collection tank for sirenin-
containing water.

Figure 9. Carboys of female plants.

Figure 10. Trays for holding female
plants in shallow layers of water during
gamete and sirenin formation.

Figure 12. Continuous automatic evaporator. Developed from Precision Scientific Company's "Precision" laboratory
evaporator. The electronic controls were
designed and built by Mr. J. Lavioletta
of the Electronic Engineering Company,
Berkeley, California.

Figure 13. Silicic acid columns.

24 hours in a continuous chloroform extractor. After reducing the chloroform sample to 50 ml., it is fractionated twice in silicic acid columns (Figure 13). The final sample, after appropriate assays, is sent on to Dr. Rapoport. In closing this part of my discussion I can only say that I hope that a year from now it will be possible to discuss the chemistry of sirenin rather than the engineering aspects of production.

When the worst of the engineering problems encountered in getting the *Allomyces* sirenin into production were solved, I cast about for another organism from which a sirenin might be obtained for a comparative study. My colleague, Professor Papenfuss, recommended the green alga *Oedogonium*. He, and also another colleague, Professor Proskauer, predicted that in certain species of *Oedogonium* I would find not only a sirenin but additional sexual hormones. With evidence obtained largely through the efforts of Dr. Erika Rawitscher-Kunkel working in my laboratory, I will now describe the observations and experiments leading

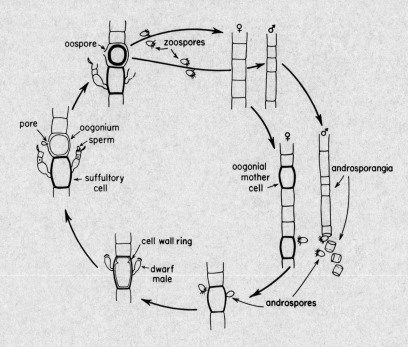

Figure 14. Diagrammatic life cycle of a heterothallic, nannandrous species of *Oedogonium*.

to the conclusion that at least four hormonal steps are involved in the sexual reproduction of one of the species we have studied.

The life cycle of this species as it is currently given in the literature (Smith, 1955) is shown diagrammatically in Figure 14. The vegetative body consists of unbranched male and female filaments of green, cylindrical, rigid cells. Under appropriate nutritional conditions, certain cells in the female filament become quite dense and slightly elliptical; these are the oögonial mother cells. In the male filament, series of short cells appear—these are the androsporangia—from each of which a single, green, flagellated androspore emerges and swims vig-

orously for some hours. In the presence of female filaments, androspores perch on the oögonial mother cell and there develop into the one-celled dwarf males which cut off one or more antheridia at their apices.

In the meantime the oögonial mother cell divides at the upper end to give rise to the rounded oögonium containing a single egg and the lower suffultory cell to which the dwarf males are attached. Each antheridium releases a motile sperm. Following fertilization, the zygote secretes a heavy wall and turns orange. When it germinates, four zoöspores are released, two developing into female filaments and two into male filaments.

Let us now turn a physiological eye

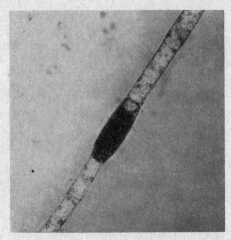

Figure 15. Oögonial mother cell suspended in India ink showing gelatinous sheath.

protoplasts and barrel shapes. We found, on suspending filaments in diluted India ink that all the cells are encased in a very thin sheath of gelatinous, transparent material which is significantly thicker around the oögonial mother cell (Figure 15). This we will return to later.

Oögonial mother cells also secrete a sirenin which leads to a concentration of very vigorously moving androspores around each oögonial mother cell (Figure 16). Two experiments amply support the functioning of a sirenin here. If a female filament is embedded in a small block of agar which in turn is immersed in a dish of androspore-producing male plants, then androspores gather in great numbers about the bit of agar and continue to do so for periods of up to 3 weeks, if not longer. If water in which oögonial mother cells have developed is put into capillary tubes or solidified with agar, then androspores are attracted to the agar or into the capillary as well as clustering about the ends of the capillary. This androspore

on this life cycle. First, however, let us consider two questions for which we have no answers. Why do only certain cells, more or less regularly along a filament, become oögonial mother cells? And how are these certain cells singled out for reproductive activity?

The oögonial mother cells are characterized by more than their denser

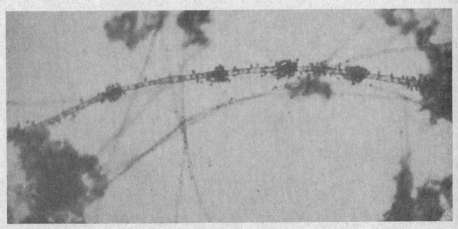

Figure 16.   Attraction of androspores to oögonial mother cells.

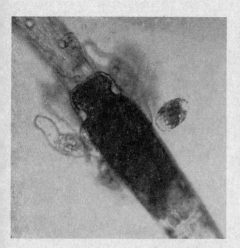

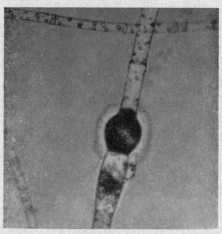

Figure 17. Oögonial mother cell with cell wall ring at upper end preparatory to final stages of cell division. Note androspore and dwarf males.

Figure 18. Gelatinous sheath around oögonium with apex of a dwarf male embedded in the gel. Sheath made visible with India ink.

sirenin is the first hormone we postulate.

Some of the androspores attach to the oögonial mother cells and proceed to develop into dwarf males during the next 15 hours or so. At the same time but taking about 22 hours, the oögonial mother cell prepares for cell division by secreting the typical cell wall ring (Figure 17) while internally nuclear and protoplasmic divisions occur (Smith, 1955). In the next hour or so the cell wall ring stretches upward to form the wall of the oögonium and a transverse cell wall is formed at the former position of the ring cutting off the lower suffultory cell to which the dwarf males are attached and the upper oögonium which becomes encased in a very thick gelatinous sheath (Figure 18).

None of this process of oögonial mother cell division takes place unless androspores do attach. The best test

of this obligatory relationship that we have so far devised is to embed fertile filaments with and without attached androspores in blocks of soft agar and then place the agar blocks in liquid containing androspore-producing male plants. Female filaments with attached androspores proceed to divide into oögonia and suffultory cells; those without do not divide even though the agar becomes coated with androspores, many of which develop into dwarf males and produce sperm. If subsequently the agar is cut open permitting access of androspores to the oögonial mother cells, oögonium formation takes place as usual. We conclude that the dwarf male provides a stimulus, presumably hormonal in nature, that triggers oögonial mother cell division and gel formation about the oögonium.

Growth and development of androspores into dwarf males, including antheridial formation and sperm discharge, is not dependent on attachment to the female plant. It will take place on the surface of agar blocks as noted above and has sometimes been observed to occur on the surface of culture solutions containing only male plants. The direction of development of attached dwarf males is, however, controlled by the female plant, presumably by a hormone emanating from the oögonial mother cell. When only two or three androspores attach to an oögonial mother cell, they almost always do so in the upper portion and grow upwards so that their apices become embedded in the gel surrounding the oögonium (Figure 18).

When a great many androspores are permitted access to the female filaments, they attach all over the oögonial mother cell and even occasionally to the cells immediately adjacent to the oögonial mother cell. They then develop in a very regular directional pattern (Figure 19). All those attached above the lower one-half to two-thirds of the oögonial mother cell grow upwards while those attached below grow downwards. When dwarf males develop on agar they grow as straight rods; moreover they show no directional response to the nearby oögonial mother cell (Figure 20).

If we now return to Figure 18 it is obvious that when sperm emerge from the antheridia they will be in the gel surrounding the oögonium. In effect, they are trapped and prevented from dispersing themselves in the surrounding free liquid medium. Although the sperm are trapped in the gel, they are not immobilized. They move very slowly in what appears at times to be sporadic jerks and at other times a creeping motion. The several

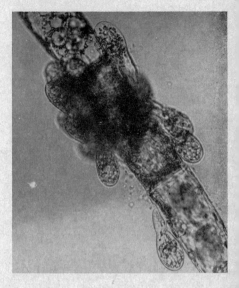

Figure 19. Developing dwarf males on an oögonial mother cell.

sperm often seen randomly distributed in the gel sooner or later end up congregated in the vicinity of the pore leading into the oögonium (Figure 21). Eventually one sperm finds the pore

Figure 20. Dwarf males on agar.

naturally gel-free oögonia as do the androspores to the oögonial mother cells in the species discussed today.

In conclusion, I think it is safe to say that the elucidation of this life cycle at the biochemical level is a considerable challenge. It is my hope that my laboratory will have some progress to report during the next year on the chemical characteristics of the sirenin that lures androspores to perch on oögonial mother cells.

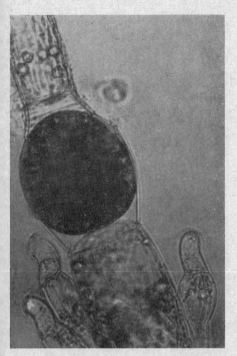

Figure 21. Two sperm (one not clearly evident) hovering in the vicinity of the entrance pore to the oögonium (upper right).

and presumably enters (Figure 22). (We have never seen one enter in this species but have observed it in another species.) We interpret the congregating of the sperm about the pore to indicate the operation of a second sirenin in this species. We know from our own observations and the recently published report of Hoffman (1960) that free-swimming sperm of another species of *Oedogonium* do respond to

Figure 22. A sperm entering an oögonium (just below large dwarf male in upper right).

Questions and Answers

QUESTION: In the simpler species, what controls the development of oögonia and antheridia?

ANSWER: We don't know. If you take the heterothallic species, you can grow the female plants quite separate from the male plants and then subject them to low nitrogen conditions after you have obtained a reasonable amount of vegetative growth. In the culture of female plants, oögonia develop; in the culture of male plants, antheridia develop. There is no interaction for the development of the sex structures in these less complex species. This method of simply putting them in low nitrogen conditions is one that has been used for years in causing algae, and sometimes fungi, to become reproductive. We don't know what changes in the organism that finally makes it quit dividing vegetatively and then make these reproductive cells.

Of course you are familiar with Raper's work on *Achlya*. In it there is an interaction between the two sexes, one causing the induction of something in the other, and that one causing induction of a further step in the first organism.

QUESTION: What became of the gel surrounding the oögonium in the other species of *Oedogonium?*

ANSWER: I can't answer your question because it has been hard enough working on just one species. We do have about a dozen different species of *Oedogonium* in the culture collection. Many of them are in pure culture, but each one is a problem in its own right, and takes too many months to work out. We pushed this one because we think we can go into production, so to speak, on the substance that causes the attraction of the androspores. All we want is enough to see if it has any chemical relationship to the substance from the fungus. We want to see if there are any generalities here of the things that do this trick.

I might mention a rather interesting point. I have been talking to zoologists off and on about this kind of interaction at the gamete level seeming to be restricted to the plant kingdom. I do not know of an authenticated case any place in the animal kingdom of interaction at the gamete level, that is, bringing them together. I am not talking about membrane reactions when they finally meet. Animals seem to prefer to work at the organism level.

REFERENCES

Emerson, Ralph, and C. W. Wilson, 1954. Interspecific hybrids and the cytogenetics and cyto-taxonomy of *Euallomyces*. Mycologia, *46*:393-434.

Hofman, L. R., 1960. Chemtaxis of *Oedogonium* sperms. Southwest Nat., *5*:111-116.

Jaffe, L. F., 1958. Morphogenesis in lower plants. Ann. Rev. Plant Physiol., *9*:358-84.

Machlis, L., 1958a. Evidence for a sexual hormone in *Allomyces*. Physiol. Plant, *11*:181-192.

————, 1958b. A study of sirenin, the chemetactic sexual hormone from the watermold *Allomyces*. Physiol. Plantarum, *11*:845-854.

Naf, U., 1958. On the physiology of antheridium formation in the bracken fern (*Pteridium aquilinum* (L) Kuhn). Physiol. Plantarum, *11*:728-746.

————, 1960. On the control of antheridium formation in the fern species *Lygodium japonicum*. Proc. Soc. Exp. Biol. and Med., *105*: 82-86.

Raper, J. R., 1952. Chemical regulation of sexual processes in the thallophytes. Bot. Rev., *18*:447-545.

————, 1954. "Life cycles, sexuality and sexual mechanisms in the fungi." In *Sex in Microorganisms*. D. H. Wenrich, I. F. Lewis, J. R. Raper, eds. AAAS, Washington, pp. 42-81.

————, 1957. Hormones and sexuality in lower plants. Sym. Soc. Exp. Biol., *11*:143-165.

————, 1960. The control of sex in fungi. Am. J. Bot., *47*:794-808.

Rothschild, L., 1956. *Fertilization*. London, Methuen and Co., Ltd., ix + 170.

Smith, G. M., 1955. *Cryptogamic Botany*. Vol. I. *Algae and Fungi,* 2nd ed. New York, McGraw-Hill Book Co., Inc., ix + 546.

Note added in proof. Since this talk was given it has been reported that the motile sperm of *Campanularia* are attracted to the female gonangium (Miller, R. L., and L. Nelson, 1962. Biol. Bull., *123*:477).

Some of the research on *Oedogonium* has also been published (Machlis, L., 1962. The nutrition of certain species of the green alga *Oedogonium*. Am. J. Bot., *49*: 171-177; and Rawitsher-Kunkel, E., and L. Machlis, 1962. The hormonal integration of sexual reproduction in *Oedogonium*. Am. J. Bot., *49*: 177-183).

Estrogen-like Substances in Plants

E. M. BICKOFF
Western Regional Research Laboratory,[1] *Albany 10, California*

THE TOPIC that I have been invited to discuss, estrogen-like substances in plants, is a broad one on which much information of a general nature has been accumulating for the past 35 years. However, our knowledge of specific substances responsible for estrogenic activity of many of these active plants is still limited and fragmentary.

Interest of animal nutritionists in naturally occurring plant estrogens is related to two opposing questions: (a) What potential difficulties, such as interference with reproduction, may arise due to the presence of estrogens in natural feedstuffs? and (b) will natural feeds of high estrogen content be able to produce the same beneficial effects, such as increased rate of growth, increased feed efficiency, and improvement of meat quality, that are now being obtained with synthetic estrogens such as diethylstilbestrol?

This paper will briefly report on types of plants that have been found to be estrogenic, and then indicate our present knowledge regarding chemical structures of identified plant estrogens.

My interest in this field stems from work on the estrogen-like compounds found in forage crops, and I plan to present the subject of forage estrogens in somewhat more detail, indicating first what has been accomplished to date. Then, I will describe the lines of investigation being pursued in our Laboratory, including cooperative investigations underway with other research groups. These include a study of the relation of plant estrogens to

[1] A laboratory of the Western Utilization Research and Development Division, Agricultural Research Service, U. S. Department of Agriculture.

rate of animal growth, now in progress in the Animal Science Department at Oregon State University. Finally, I shall conclude by suggesting several lines of work that might be undertaken profitably in the field of plant estrogens.

Plants Reported Estrogenic

In the female animal, the follicular hormone or estrogen is produced by the ovaries. Its production marks the beginning of ovulation and the estrus cycle. The basis of the Allen-Doisy test for estrogenic substances is the determination of the onset of estrus in the test animal, by observation of the appearance of cornified epithelial cells in vaginal smears. Removal of the ovaries stops sex development and secondary sexual characteristics do not appear or, if present, tend to disappear. A reverse effect can be induced by administering ovarian extracts or estrogens.

In order to demonstrate the presence of estrogenic substances in plants, the first step has generally been to carry out tests with plant extracts injected subcutaneously into mice or rats and to observe their effect by the Allen-Doisy technique. One of the first references in this field is that of Loewe (1926). In his work, ovaries of the water rose and of willow catkins were air-dried and extracted with ether. These extracts, after being freed of undesired constituents, were injected into ovariectomized mice and were found to produce estrus. In more recent work, increase in uterine weight of ovariectomized or immature female mice or rats is usually employed to measure estrogenic activity. Material under investigation can either be fed by incorporating it into the diet or it can be injected subcutaneously, usually as an oily suspension.

In a review on "Estrogens in Plants," Bradbury and White (1954) reported that over 50 different plants have been found to be estrogenic. Although this activity has in a few cases been confirmed by several groups of investigators, very few plants have thus far yielded crystalline estrogens. High activities have been reported for garlic (*Allium sativum*, L.), milkweed or butterfly weed (*Asclepias tuberosa*, L.), and oats (*Avena sativa*, L.). Other common plant materials that have been reported to be estrogenic include coffee, licorice, sunflower, wheat, barley, apple, parsley, the fruit flesh of cherry and plum, rhubarb leaves, yeast, willow flowers, sage, rye grass, and potato tubers. In none of these cases is the active principle known. A number of legume forage plants have also been reported to be estrogenic. Considerable work has been done with forage estrogens; at least five estrogenic compounds are known to occur.

Tulip bulbs are also high in estrogenic activity. During the last months of World War II, there was a severe shortage of food in Holland. According to Coussens and Sierens (1949), large quantities of tulip bulbs were eaten during that period. As a result, many women showed manifestations of estrogen imbalance, such as uterine bleeding and abnormalities of the menstrual cycle. Coussens and Sierens, however, made no attempt to determine the nature of the active substance.

Estrogenic activity has also been reported in bacteria (Pedersen-Bjergaard, 1933) and in commercial animal rations (Zarrow et al., 1953). Soybean meal, a standard feed ingredient, contains at least two estrogenic substances.

The report by Bradbury and White (1954) also listed plants not showing estrogenic activity when extracts were tested. These included alfalfa and white clover. We have recently isolated the plant estrogen, coumestrol, as well as several isoflavonoid estrogen-like substances from both of these plants. This illustrates that inaccurate conclusions can be made regarding the presence or absence of an estrogen in a particular species of plant, when the estrogen content of the plant varies considerably during its growing season.

Isolation of Estrogens

Naturally occurring estrogens of animals are all chemically related derivatives of cyclopentenophenanthrene having the same basic structure but differing in the number and position of substituents. These estrogens are shown in Figure 1.

Estrone is not the most active of the estrogenic substances, but it usually is the standard for comparison of activity of related compounds. Estrone is much more effective by injection than by oral administration. Estradiol is about four to eight times as effective as estrone. Estriol is only about 1/10 as active but its action is somewhat more protracted. Equilenin is 1/10 and equilin 1/3 as active as estrone. Equilenin and equilin are found only in pregnant mares' urine.

Estrogenic constituents have now been isolated from several plants, and it is clear that although these constituents are in some cases identical with normal animal estrogens, this identity is by no means universal. Estrogen-like compounds with quite different structures have also been isolated.

Animal estrogens from plant sources. The first isolation and characterization of an estrogen from a plant source was accomplished by Butenandt and Jacobi (1933). In this case, the compound proved to be identical to one of the normal animal estrogens. They extracted the residual cake left after pressing palm kernels, and from 50 kilograms of the press cake they obtained 2.4 kilograms of an oil which was soluble in methanol and had an estrogenic activity of 1,000,000 mouse units[2] per gram. The oil was saponified, and the nonsaponifiable fraction was distilled and hydrolyzed with acid. After crystallization from aqueous alcohol, 18 milligrams of estrone was obtained. It was characterized by melting point, optical rotation, ultraviolet absorption spectra, and the preparation of derivatives which were compared with authentic samples. In addition, biologic activity was equal to that of estrone isolated from urine.

---

[2] A mouse or rat unit is defined as the minimum amount of an estrogenic substance required to produce full estrous response in 100% of animals tested.

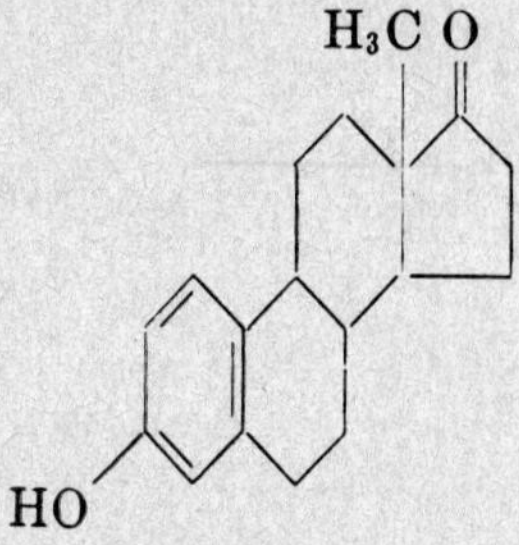

I
Estrone

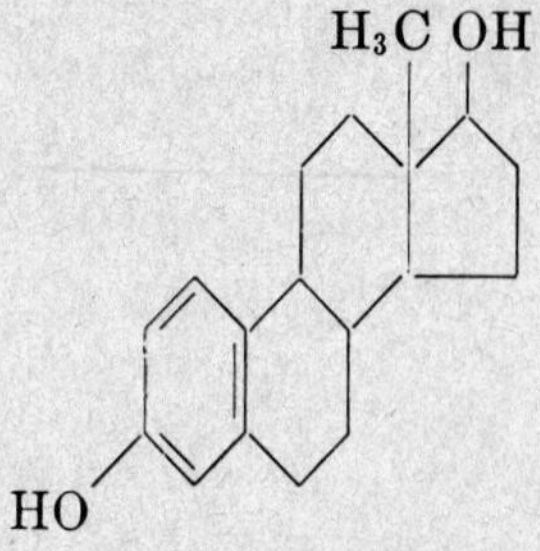

II
"α"-Estradiol

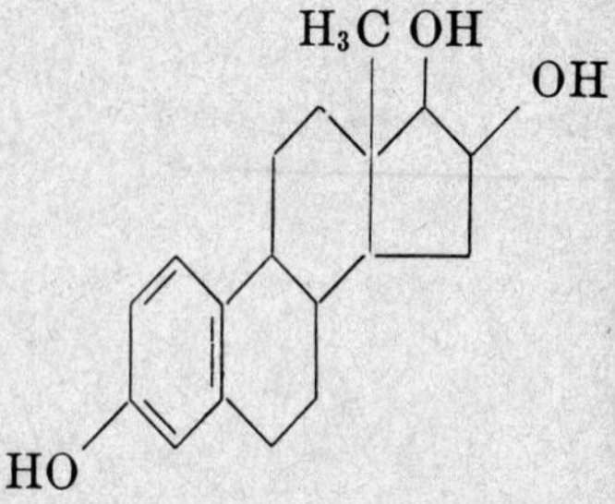

III
Estriol

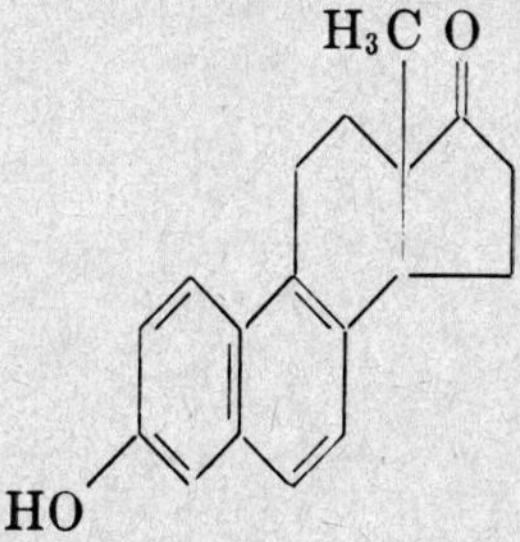

IV
Equilenin

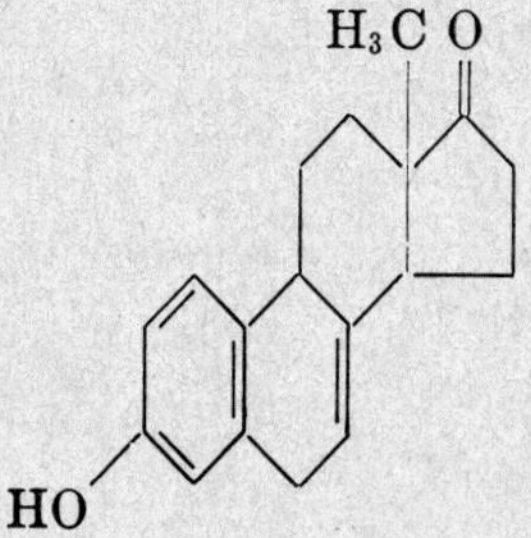

V
Equilin

Figure 1. The natural animal estrogens.

This work was of interest and importance because it demonstrated for the first time that a sex hormone normally secreted by animals may also be a normal constituent of certain plant products.

Closely following Butenandt and Jacobi's isolation of estrone from palm kernels, Skarzynski (1933, a.b.) reported isolation of a crystalline estrogen from willow flowers. He obtained 7.5 milligrams of crystals from 65 kilograms of flowers and found that they closely resembled estriol, one of the natural sex hormones originally isolated from pregnant mare urine. Identity of the two substances was verified by microscopic appearance, solubilities, ultraviolet absorption, and melting point. The melting point of willow estrogen was depressed only 1° C. by estriol isolated from urine, and melting points of the respective acetates were identical.

Biological activity of Skarzynski's product was, however, only one quarter that of the estriol he prepared from urine, but this difference may not be significant in view of the limited accuracy of the Allen-Doisy technique at that time.

El Ridi and Wafa (1947), using the procedure of Butenandt and Jacobi, obtained an oil from the pollen of date palm (*Dactylifera palmae*, L.) insoluble in water and showing 40% of the estrogenic activity of estradiol. This oil gave color reactions similar to estrone and had its maximum ultraviolet absorption at a wave length similar to that of estrogenic hormones (282 millimicrons). It is unfortunate, in view of the high activity of the extract, that they were not able to obtain a crystalline product or characterize the active substance by the preparation of a crystalline derivative.

In another attempt, pollen grains of the date palm (*Phoenix dactylifera*, L.) were extracted by Hassan and Wafa (1947), and their water-soluble product showed color reactions and ultraviolet absorption resembling estrone. Unfortunately, however, here again isolation was not carried to a definite compound.

Presence of sterols in a large number of plants has been quite well established, although in a number of cases they have not been completely purified or adequately characterized. It is noteworthy that sterols have been isolated from several of the plants listed as estrogenic by Bradbury and White (1954). It would not be surprising if these sterols were accompanied by small amounts of steroid estrogens, either as normal plant constituents or perhaps formed by some biologic oxidation process from the sterols. Alternatively, it may be possible for test animals to transform certain sterols in part into estrogens, or estrogens may arise by oxidation of sterols during the course of the isolation procedure.

Miroestrol, the estrogenic substance of *Pueraria mirifica*: Presence of estrogenic material in the tuberous roots of a Siamese, woody, climbing plant found in northern Thailand was first reported by Vatna (1939) after attention had been drawn to the fact that the roots were used locally as a rejuvenating drug. An, alcohol extract of the root had a potency equivalent to 500,000 mouse units per gram. Isolation from this source of a highly active, pure substance was described by Schoeller, Dohrn, and Hohlweg (1940). A preliminary chemical investigation of the compound was carried out by Butenandt (1940) who reported the molecular formula as $C_{19}H_{20}O_6$, but he was not able to establish the structure. The plant was at that time believed to be *Butea superba*, but it has since been recognized as a new species and named *Pueraria mirifica* (Bounds and Pope, 1960). Structure of the compound was determined by X-ray crystallographic analysis (Taylor, Hodgkin, and Rollett, 1960) and it proved to be distinctly different than that of animal estrogens (Figure 2). Chemical properties of the compound, which was named miroestrol, have been

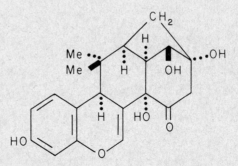

Figure 2. Structure of miroestrol (Bounds and Pope, 1960).

recently described by Bounds and Pope (1960), and the estrogenic activity determined. When given subcutaneously in multiple doses, it is as potent as estradiol-17β, and orally it is more than three times as potent as diethylstilbestrol in producing an increase in uterine weight in the immature mouse (Jones and Pope, 1960).

Isolation of this estrogen marked an important advance in our knowledge of plant estrogens, as it was the first demonstration of the presence in a plant of a highly potent substance not identical with normal steroid estrogens of the animal world.

Beta-bitter acid, an estrogenic factor in hops. Zenisek and Bednar (1960) have recently reported that concentrates prepared from hop extracts are estrogenic and that beta-bitter acid (Figure 3) has a high estrogenic activity. This acid is a mixture of four substances. Three of them, lupulon, colupulon, and adlupulon, have the same basic structure, differing only in the side chain. The fourth, prelupulon, is of an unknown chemical constitution. These workers next propose to ascertain in what way the four constituents of beta-bitter acid contribute to its estrogenic activity and

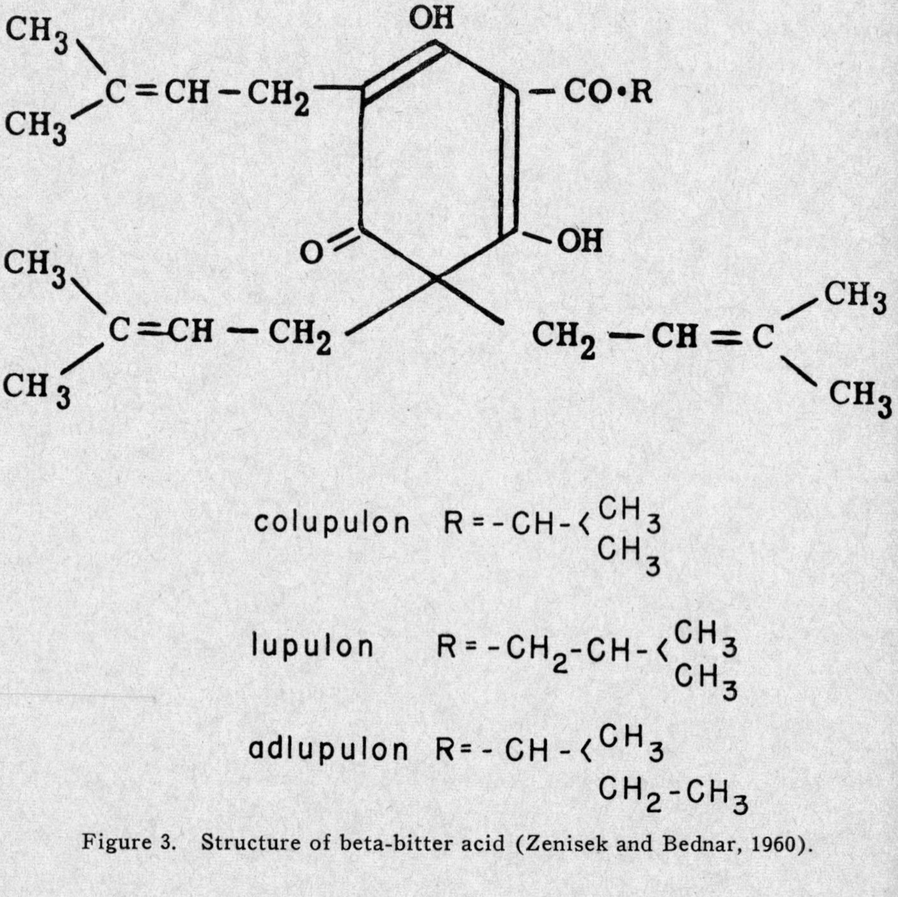

Figure 3.   Structure of beta-bitter acid (Zenisek and Bednar, 1960).

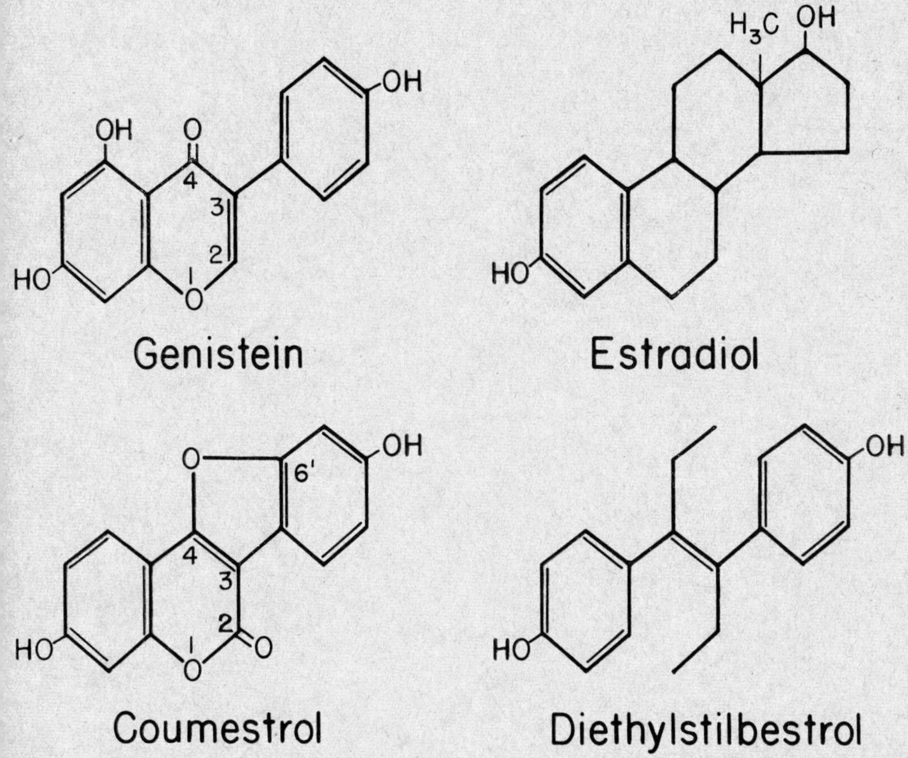

Genistein

Estradiol

Coumestrol

Diethylstilbestrol

Figure 4. Structural formulas of genistein, estradiol, coumestrol, and diethylstilbestrol.

whether alpha-acid which has the same skeletal structure as the components of the beta-acid complex is also estrogenically active.

Estrogens in forage crops. A very significant development in plant estrogen research came about during the period from 1941 to 1951 when the cause of infertility in sheep grazed on subterranean clover in Australia was traced to the presence of an estrogen in forage. These estrogens were subsequently isolated and identified by Bradbury and White (1951). Using the mouse uterine weight bio-

assay to guide them, Bradbury and White (1951) finally isolated (from about 9,000 pounds of clover) the estrogens which were responsible for the reproductive problem in sheep. Genistein (Figure 4) was shown to be the principal estrogen and was about 1/50,000 as active as diethylstilbestrol.[3] Genistin, the glycoside of genistein, had earlier been shown to be a constituent of soybean meal (Walter, 1941), but its estrogenic activity was not known at that time.

---

[3] Diethylstilbestrol has an estrogenic activity of one million mouse units per gram.

Formononetin and biochanin A (Figure 5) have also been shown to be constituents of subterranean clover and these two estrogens, together with genistein, have also been found in red clover (Pope and Wright, 1954).

Daidzin has been found in soybean meal (Walz, 1931), and we have recently found its aglycone, daidzein (Figure 5), in subterranean and red clovers, alfalfa, and ladino clover. We have also found biochanin A in alfalfa but not in ladino clover and formononetin and genistein in alfalfa and ladino clover (Guggolz, Livingston, and Bickoff, 1961). The relative estrogenic activity of these compounds as compared to diethylstilbestrol (Table 1) was determined by Cheng et al. (1954). Their activities are approximately the same, except for formononetin which is less active than the other three. As indicated earlier, even the most potent is much less active than diethylstilbestrol.

This low activity led Cheng and Burroughs to make the following comment regarding these compounds (Cheng and Burroughs, 1959) : "Because of the very low potency of these compounds, it may be difficult for isoflavones to account for all the estrogenic activity of plant extracts, especially in the case of subterranean clover. It is possible that some biological transformation of these compounds may occur with the production of more active intermediates. Until more information about the metabolism of the isoflavones is known, however, isoflavones per se probably should be considered as a class of naturally occurring estrogens of plant origin."

In our laboratory, we have recently succeeded in isolating a new estrogen from ladino clover in crystalline form. This material is different in structure from any of the known animal estrogens. It is also different from the isoflavones previously isolated from

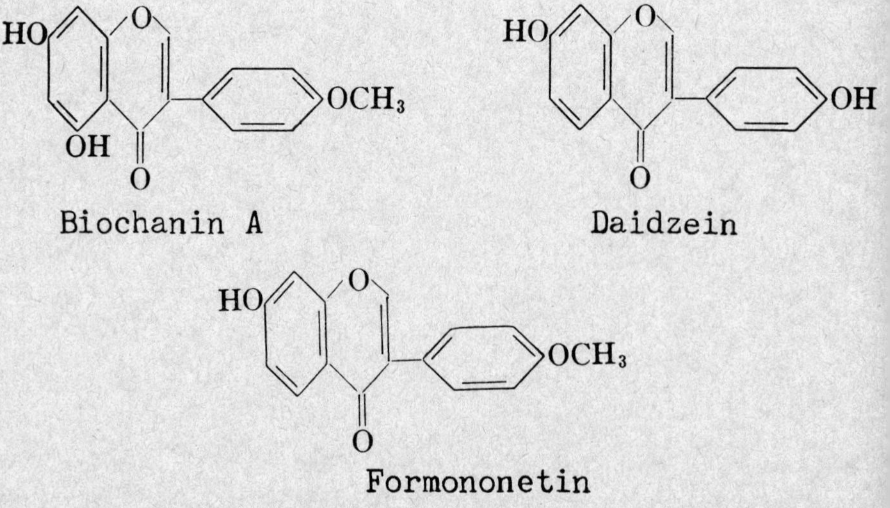

Figure 5.   Structures of biochanin A, formononetin, and daidzein.

TABLE 1. Estrogenic activity of some isoflavone derivatives[1]

No. of mice	Treatment	Average uterine weight	Approx. potency[2]
		mg.	
6	Normal control	6.4 ± 0.8	
6	Biochanin A, 2.5 mg.	20.9 ± 3.1	0.033
5	Daidzein, 2.5 mg.	26.6 ± 4.1	0.042
6	Formononetin, 2.5 mg.	8.9 ± 1.2	0.009
5	Genistein, 2.5 mg.	19.3 ± 1.3	0.030
6	Stilbestrol, 0.01 μg.	9.4 ± 0.8	
6	Stilbestrol, 0.02 μg.	15.7 ± 1.5	
6	Stilbestrol, 0.04 μg.	22.2 ± 2.1	
5	Stilbestrol, 0.08 μg.	46.2 ± 4.7	

[1] Data from Cheng and Burroughs (1959).
[2] Expressed as micrograms of diethylstilbestrol activity.

forages. Because of its coumarin-like structure (Figure 4) we have named this compound Coumestrol (Bickoff et al., 1957, 1958a, 1958b). Coumestrol, administered orally or subcutaneously, produces an increase in uterine weight in immature or overiectomized mice. It is about 30 times more potent than genistein, but still considerably less active than the natural animal estrogens or diethylstilbestrol. To date, we have found coumestrol in every legume that we have tested (Lyman et al., 1959).

Emmens (1941) has suggested that many substances which exhibit estrogenic activity are proestrogens; that these substances are metabolized in the body, and that it is a metabolic product that is the true estrogenic substance. According to Emmens, estrogens can be classified into two groups, based on the ratio of the median effective dose required to produce vaginal cornification in ovariectomized mice when the estrogen is given by subcutaneous injection to the dose required when given by intravaginal instillation. This ratio is called the systemic/local or the S/L ratio. Proestrogens have an S/L ratio of approximately 1, and true estrogens have an S/L ratio of the order of 100. Emmens very kindly evaluated coumestrol for us by his test. He found an S/L ratio of approximately one; thus coumestrol should be considered a proestrogen that is metabolized in the body into a true estrogen. According to Biggers (1958), the fact that a compound has an S/L ratio of about unity is no direct proof that it is a proestrogen. This proof requires actual demonstration that a metabolite has sufficient estrogenic potency, and this would require an isotopically labeled compound for study. So far, this has not been done for coumestrol or genistein.

According to Whalley (quoted by Biggers, 1958) estrogenic activity of coumestrol can be attributed to the stilbene-like structure of this compound, analogous to that of diethylstilbestrol. This relationship is shown in

Figure 4. The fact that coumestrol is more than 30 times as active as the closely related estrogenic isoflavone, genistein, is probably due to the fact that the oxygen atom at position 4 of the isoflavone is primarily ketonic, which results in a single rather than a double bond in the 3, 4 position.

Bradbury (1953) remarked on the striking similarity between naturally occurring estrogenic isoflavones, one of which is genistein, and the 3-phenyl-4-hydroxycoumarins. In this connection, Biggers quotes Bate-Smith (Biggers, 1958) to the effect that coumestrol may be derived in the plant by rearrangement of the isoflavonol corresponding to daidzein with ring closure to the 6′ position.

More recently, Grisebach (1959) has suggested a biogenetic scheme which explains the formation of all flavones, isoflavones, and coumestrol found in red clover.

Estrogen Inhibitors and Potentiators

A number of compounds have been reported as capable of blocking various actions of estrogens in the vagina and uterus. Emmens, Cox, and Martin (1960) reported that dimethylstilbestrol and certain steroids such as 19-nortestosterone inhibited estradiol in intravaginal tests of cornification in the spayed mouse vagina. Certain plants have also been reported to contain estrogen inhibitors. Extracts of the white bean (*Phaseolus vulgaris* L.) were reported to inhibit estrus (Belak and Szathmary, 1937).

Ershoff (1956) has described beneficial effects of alfalfa on ovarian development of immature rats fed massive does of alphaestradiol. We have found that extracts from certain alfalfa samples act as estrogen inhibitors, depressing the response that would normally be obtained by coumestrol added to the diet.

Certain other samples of alfalfa meal have been found to contain estrogen potentiators. That is, an extract of the meal having no measurable estrogenic activity in itself will greatly increase the estrogenic response of a given amount of coumestrol incorporated into the mouse diet.

Effect of Plant Estrogens on Reproduction

As mentioned earlier, current interest in forage estrogens was stimulated by serious reproductive difficulties in sheep.

In 1941 an outbreak of infertility in sheep appeared with spectacular suddenness in a large part of western Australia (Bennetts et al., 1946). Areas affected (totaling over 8,000 square miles) were all low in rainfall and the predominant pasture was subterranean clover in all of them. Since this clover had been the predominant pasture for 15 years, the sudden outbreak was difficult to explain on the basis that the clover was responsible, but this proved to be the case. A combination of wartime factors (e.g., shortage of fertilizer and bulk feed) and climatic conditions had caused a much greater intake of clover per sheep for a long period.

Symptoms included failure of ewes to conceive, stillbirth, or early death of lambs, and various disorders of the female reproductive system. Rams were not affected. Lambing percentage sometimes dropped to as low as 8%, and transfer of ewes to good nonclover grazing areas for three successive seasons did not restore fertility. It has since been found that this problem could be controlled to a considerable extent by limiting intake of clover and increasing intake of grasses which are known to be low in estrogens. However, even under the best of conditions, it has been estimated that there is a continuing chronic reproduction problem in Australian sheep, which results in about a 15% loss in the lamb crop.

In the United States there is an ever-increasing interest in forage estrogens as a result of field observations of breeding difficulties in sheep and cattle on legume forage pastures. Engle et al. (1957) of the Ohio Agricultural Experiment Station have reported that ewes grazed on ladino clover pasture conceived 3 weeks later on the average than did comparable animals grazing all season on bluegrass or birdsfoot trefoil (Table 2). In addition, their average fertility was considerably

TABLE 2. INFLUENCE OF PASTURE ON REPRODUCTION EFFICIENCY

Kind of pasture	Ewes lambing to first service
	%
Bluegrass	66
Ladino clover	41
Birdsfoot trefoil	31

[1] Data from Engle et al. (1957).

TABLE 3. INFLUENCE OF FEED ON LAMBING EFFICIENCY

Treatment	Lambing percentage	Range in days to complete lambing
Alfalfa hay	156	12
Red clover hay	110	19
Red clover pasture	110	35

[1] Data from Fox et al. (1959).

less. Estrogenic activity was detected in ladino clover and birdsfoot trefoil but not in bluegrass.

Several years ago some sheepmen in western Oregon complained that a longer lambing period and a lower lambing percentage resulted when ewes were pastured on red clover during "flushing" and breeding.

The Department of Animal Science of Oregon State University initiated studies on the effects of red clover pasture or hay on reproduction in sheep. Their work (Fox et al., 1959) clearly showed that ewes fed on red clover pasture 17 days before and 51 days after breeding had a considerably longer lambing period than ewes fed either alfalfa hay or red clover. In addition, the total lamb crop was lower for the pasture-fed animals. Fox et al. demonstrated that feeding red clover to mice caused alteration in the size of follicles in the ovaries, and they concluded that compounds present in red clover that interfere with fertility do not behave as either true estrogens or true progesterone but that some of both effects are present. In another report from Oregon State University, Fox, Kaufmes, Mason, and Oldfield (1957) found that mice fed fresh red clover or red clover hay failed to litter, further verifying that there was a substance present in the clover that interfered with reproduction (Table 4). Dr. Booth, of our Pharmacology Laboratory in Albany, has confirmed the effect of red clover in preventing reproduction in mice by feeding crude acetone extracts of red clover to mice.

TABLE 4. EFFECT OF RED CLOVER ON
LITTERING IN MICE[1]

Female treatment	No. of females that littered	No. of females not littering
Control	27	3
Red clover hay[2]..	0	30
Fresh red clover[2]	0	30

[1] Data from Fox et al. (1957).
[2] The clovers were fed as 40% of the dry weight of the diet.

Crude acetone extracts of red clover were added to a control diet at a level equivalent to 50% of the diet. He has also been able to inhibit reproduction with similar extracts of ladino clover. More recently, he prevented reproduction by feeding the pure estrogen, coumestrol. In other feeding experiments, Booth has demonstrated that the estrogen interferes with fertility of the male as well as of the female.

Similar observations have been made with the plant estrogen, genistin. Carter, Smart, and Matrone (1955) showed that when genistin was fed to mice at a level of 0.02% of the diet, premature opening of the vagina occurred and fewer litters were born. In a subsequent paper, Matrone and co-workers (1956) showed that orally administered genistin depresses the growth rate of male mice, reduces testicular weight, and suppresses spermatogenesis.

Wright (1960) reported on infertility in rabbits induced by feeding ladino clover. This research was prompted by reports from several dairy farmers in New Hampshire of reproductive failure of heifers and dairy cows fed on a diet rich in ladino clover. In each instance, substitution of a timothy hay diet quickly corrected infertility. A similar report from Israel of infertility in cows fed on alfalfa has recently appeared (Adler and Trainin, 1960).

Table 5 summarizes some observations of reproductive difficulties associated with plant hormones. It seems probable that many undiagnosed instances of reduced fertility in farm animals may be attributable to excessive ingestion of forage materials that are high in estrogenic activity.

Reproductive problems such as these could be controlled if we could produce forage of known estrogen content.

Variation in Estrogenic Activity

In order to control the estrogenic activity of forages, it will be necessary to develop a more complete understanding of normal variations in potency that can be expected to occur in forages as a result of different varieties, different stages of growth, seasons of the year, number of cuttings, and climatic conditions. Andrews and his coworkers (Pieterse and Andrews, 1956a, 1956b) at Purdue University showed that estrogen con-

TABLE 5. REPRODUCTIVE DIFFICULTIES DUE TO PLANT HORMONES

Breeding difficulties in sheep

Subterranean clover	Australia	Genistein Biochanin A
Ladino clover	Ohio	Coumestrol
Red clover	Oregon	Genistein Coumestrol Biochanin A

Breeding difficulties in cattle

Ladino clover	New Hampshire	Coumestrol
Forage and pine needles	British Columbia	............*
Alfalfa	Israel	Coumestrol

Reproductive failure in mice

Crystalline coumestrol	Albany, California
Red clover	Oregon
Genestein	North Carolina

Reproductive failure in rabbits

Ladino clover	New Hampshire

* Unknown.

tent varies tremendously during the growing season with number of cuttings and stage of development of the plant. They found by bioassay that estrogen content was highest in the first cutting and decreased in later cuttings. In one phase of their study, 56 different strains of alfalfa were analyzed (Stob et al., 1957). As expected, a wide difference in estrogenic activity of various strains was found (Table 6). Difference in the degree of estrogenic activity within varieties also occurred. Kitts and his coworkers at the University of British Columbia have also been studying variation in estrogenic activity of forages by mouse bioassay (1959a, 1959b, 1960). Their results confirm the Purdue findings that extreme variations in estrogen content occur during the growing season.

TABLE 6. UTERINE WEIGHT RESPONSE TO DIFFERENT STRAINS OF ALFALFA[1]

Alfalfa strain	Mean uterine weight
no.	mg.
Control	17.00
262	18.60
339	25.08
216	30.08
80	35.80
346	41.68
138	99.96

[1] Data from Stob et al. (1957).

TABLE 7. ESTROGENIC ACTIVITY OF FIRST CUTTINGS OF ALFALFA AT DIFFERENT STAGES OF MATURITY[1]

Date of cutting	Stage of maturity	Estimated[2] potency
		mcgm.
May 3	Vegetative	55
June 3	Prebloom	12
July 2	Full bloom	4
Aug. 1	Late bloom	21
Sept. 3	Past bloom	17

[1] Data from Kitts et al. (1959).
[2] Calculated as stilbestrol equivalents per pound of dry matter.

They found that estrogenic content was highest at the vegetative stage, tending to decrease until full bloom, and then increasing again in late bloom, when the plants are partially in the dough stage (Table 7). They concluded that estrogenic activity was not associated solely with rapid growth nor with the reproductive phase of the plant.

In a related portion of their study, four successive cuttings of alfalfa were made throughout the summer, all plants being harvested at almost the same stage of development (Table 8). Estrogenic content was high in the spring, decreased during the summer, but built up again in the fall. This differs from the findings of the Purdue group that alfalfa cuttings subsequent to the first tend to be lower in estrogenic activity. However, it should be pointed out that these apparently divergent results may indicate real differences due to climate, locality, soil conditions, and other factors.

We have been studying estrogen level as influenced by stage of growth, cutting, and season of the year (Bickoff et al., 1960a, 1960b, 1960c), and (as in the work reported above) wide differences in estrogen content were found. In general, estrogen content increased with the age of the plant. (Table 9).

In a cooperative study with Professor Roubiceck of the Arizona Experimental Station (Bickoff, 1960a), a series of sun-cured alfalfa meals was prepared and sent to our laboratory for bioassay (Table 10). Samples were taken from different fields and represent average cuttings during the period involved. The first two cuttings showed almost no activity. Estrogen content was extremely high during January

TABLE 8. ESTROGENIC ACTIVITY OF 1ST, 2ND, 3RD, AND 4TH CUTTINGS OF ALFALFA[1]

Cuttings	Date of cutting	Stage of maturity	Estimated[2] potency
			mcgm.
1	May 3	Vegetative	55
2	June 2	Vegetative	14
3	July 2	Vegetative	6
4	Aug. 15	Vegetative	43

[1] Data from Kitts et al. (1959).
[2] Calculated as stilbestrol equivalents per pound of dry matter.

TABLE 9. Estrogenic activity of alfalfa at various stages of maturity (Albany)

Age of crop	Date of sampling	Height of stand	Stage of maturity	Coumestrol equivalence
weeks		inches		mg./kg.
3	3/28	3- 6	Vegetative	4
5	4/11	4- 8	Vegetative	13
7	4/23	8-14	Vegetative	9
8	4/28	10-16	Early bud	0
9	5/5	12-20	Bud	0
10	5/16	16-24	Full bud	0
12	5/29	20-28	Prebloom	0
14	6/16	20-28	1/10 bloom	7
15	6/23	24-30	1/4 bloom	9
16	6/30	24-36	1/2 bloom	33
18	7/9	24-36	Full bloom	77
24	8/20	24-36	Dough	120
26	9/5	24-36	Seedhead	123

First growth—1958 season

and then gradually tapered off. These results may indicate the effect of temperature and length of daylight on estrogenic content in the plant.

Large difference in estrogen potency of different samples made it clear that a more comprehensive approach was needed to identify the different factors that seem to interact to control estrogen content of alfalfa. This study was undertaken through cooperative projects with the Crops Research Division of the Agricultural Research Service of the United States Department of Agriculture, and the American Dehydrators Association. Samples of five different varieties of alfalfa were grown at seven USDA Crops Research Division stations in locations ranging from Pennsylvania to California. Successive cuttings were sampled at known stages of growth and sent to the Western Regional Research Labora-

tory for analysis. The analyses have been completed and data are being analyzed. It would be premature to draw conclusions, but we can report that differences range from 0 to over 600 parts per million of coumestrol in samples cut at the 1/10 bloom stage from different locations.

TABLE 10. Estrogenic activity in sun-cured alfalfa grown in Arizona and cut at 1/2 to 3/4 bloom

Dates of growth 1957-58	Average uterine weight
	mg.
11/9 - 12/6	11.2
12/7 - 1/4	10.8
1/5 - 2/5	102.6
2/6 - 3/5	41.3
3/6 - 4/3	15.0
4/4 - 5/5	20.1

Another phase of this investigation relates to estrogen content of commercially dehydrated alfalfa as determined by chemical assay. Through a cooperative arrangement with two alfalfa dehydrator operators, commercially grown alfalfa was sampled during the growing period and then harvested and dehydrated at the peak estrogen level. As the alfalfa matured, coumestrol content rose well beyond the level at which it is normally harvested (Table 11). About 12 tons of highly estrogenic alfalfa meal was obtained in this way. The meal has been used in studies on growth promotion, which will be discussed below.

TABLE 11. INCREASE IN COUMESTROL CONTENT OF COMMERCIALLY GROWN ALFALFA[1]

Date cut	Material	Time since last cutting	Coumestrol
		weeks	*p.p.m.*
8/9/60	Field	5	15
8/16/60	"	6	52
8/23/60	"	7	136
8/30/60	"	8	170
9/6/60	"	9	230
9/12/60	Field chop	10	215
9/12/60	Dehydrated		209 (m.f.b.)

[1] By chemical assay

Effect of Plant Estrogens on Rate of Growth

Burroughs and co-workers reported as early as 1955 (Hale et al., 1955) that feeding 5 to 10 milligrams of diethylstilbestrol per animal daily to cattle resulted in an increase of about 20% in rate of gain and increased feed efficiency. Since then, there has developed a tremendous interest in the use of synthetic hormones to stimulate rate and efficiency of gain in animals and the practice has become widely accepted. Synthetic estrogens are now being fed to or implanted in more than 80% of fattening steers in this country.

It would be of considerable theoretical interest and perhaps of economic importance to ascertain whether forage estrogens might also be capable of accelerating the rate of growth of animals. The very fact that some forages contain enough natural estrogen to produce negative effects in breeding animals suggests a positive potential in fattening steers, wethers, poultry, and other livestock. As Andrews (1958b) has suggested, if a level of estrogenic activity could be obtained in a forage that would stimulate growth or other functions, great benefits would accrue to the forage producer, processor, and user. The importance of developing alternative sources of growth promoters and fatteners is underlined by the fact that the use of diethylstilbestrol for poultry was banned by the F.D.A. when residues were found in the tissues of treated birds; certain restrictions also have been placed upon its use for larger animals.

From the reported stilbestrol equivalence of the various forage crops it may be difficult to understand the magnitude of estrogenic potency with respect to animal growth promotion sometimes attributed to them. Kitts (1959) reported stilbestrol equivalences of alfalfa samples as ranging from almost nil to a high of 55 micrograms per pound of dry matter. Assuming that a useful daily intake of stilbestrol for the beef steer is 10 milligrams, it can be calculated that to obtain this amount of estrogenic activity a steer would have to consume almost 200 pounds daily of dry matter from this alfalfa.

Nevertheless, this may still be of great importance, since the mouse test may not accurately reflect the relative estrogenicity of stilbestrol vs. plant estrogen to the beef animal. Fermentative changes in the rumen may increase the activity of plant estrogens, in a manner suggested by Pieterse and Andrews' earlier work (1956a). Another possibility is that the estrogen-like compound may be metabolized within the animal body into a more potent growth-promoting substance. Cumulative effects in the animal body might thus be greater with plant estrogens than with diethylstilbestrol. Cheng et al., at Iowa (1953), recognized these same discrepancies, but they could not escape the observed fact of apparent beneficial effects of plant estrogens.

Because of lack of large enough supplies of pure plant estrogens for large animal feeding experiments, their effectiveness in promoting growth of steers and wethers and in fattening poultry has not been satisfactorily proven as yet. However, indirect evidence is increasing to make a fairly convincing picture.

For example, workers at Iowa State University (Story et al., 1957) fed a crude estrogenic extract from clover hay to fattening lambs. The fortified ration contained about 2 to 3 micrograms of equivalent stilbestrol activity per pound of ration. The clover extract promoted a rate of gain of approximately 10% over the control. In an attempt to substantiate this effect more conclusively, these researchers also performed similar experiments on a limited scale with the purified plant estrogen, genistin, obtained from soybean meal, and again obtained measur-

TABLE 12. WEIGHT GAINS OF LAMBS FED LOW LEVELS OF STILBESTROL AND GENISTIN[1]

| | Addition per lb. of a basal ration | | | | |
| | Micrograms stilbestrol | | | | Milligrams genistin |
	None	1.5	3.0	6.0	200
Avg. daily gain (lbs.)	0.46	0.58	0.53	0.49	0.53

[1] Data from Story et al. (1957). Animals individually fed for 42 days.

ably increased growth rates (Table 12). The addition of 200 milligrams of genistin per pound of ration was equivalent in estrogenic activity to 3 micrograms of stilbestrol per pound. The addition of the pure genistin to the diet resulted in a 15% increase in rate of gain.

One of the most positive evidences of weight gain stimulation in steers fed alfalfa naturally high in estrogenic activity was obtained by Matsushima (1959) at the University of Nebraska (Table 13). He showed that a daily intake of 5 pounds of this alfalfa produced the same daily weight gain in pounds (2.46) as did the addition of stilbestrol to the diet (2.47). Lower amounts of alfalfa were also effective but to a lesser extent. When stilbestrol and dehydrated alfalfa were combined as a supplement, rates of gain were only slightly better than when either was administered alone.

Perhaps the most conclusive studies on the growth promoting effect of high-estrogen alfalfa are now being conducted by the Animal Science Department at Oregon State University. Oldfield, Fox, and Bickoff (1960) fed two samples of dehydrated alfalfa meal which showed potencies of 111 and 23 mg. of coumestrol per kiligram to growing lambs. When fed the high-estrogen meal wether lambs gained significantly faster than those on the low-estrogen meal and ewe lambs significantly more slowly (Table 14). Federal grades at slaughter indicated little difference in the lambs on the high and low-estrogen meals, although there was a tendency toward greater fatness in the high-estrogen fed group. Organoleptic tests conducted by a trained taste panel showed significant differences in tenderness, juiciness, and texture between the two treatments—all in favor of the high-estrogen-fed lambs.

TABLE 13. AVERAGE DAILY GAINS OF STEERS IN TWO FEEDING TESTS[1]

Protein supplement	1 lb. soybean oil meal	0.5 lb. soybean oil meal and 1.25 lbs. dehydrated alfalfa	2.5 lbs. dehydrated alfalfa	5.0 lbs. dehydrated alfalfa
Without stilbestrol in ration	2.07	2.30	2.41	2.46
With stilbestrol in ration	2.47	2.59	2.64	2.64
Percent increase in gain by adding stilbestrol	19.3	12.6	9.5	7.3

[1] Data from Matsushima (1959).

TABLE 14. EFFECT OF HIGH-ESTROGEN DEHYDRATED ALFALFA MEAL ON
WEIGHT GAINS IN WETHER LAMBS

Meal	Coumestrol content	Protein content	Average total gain (56 days)
	p.p.m.	percent	pounds
High-estrogen	111	20.5	47.2 ± 7.5[1]
Low-estrogen	23	21.7	38.8 ± 3.9[1]

[1] Standard deviation.

The high-estrogen meal prepared during the USDA-ADA cooperative study is being employed in an experiment to confirm these findings. The results at the end of 6 weeks on test are shown in Table 15. Three meals were used: low-estrogen alfalfa containing 20 p.p.m. of coumestrol, high-estrogen alfalfa containing 210 p.p.m. of coumestrol, and a blend of equal parts of these meals that contained about 110 p.p.m. of coumestrol. Each meal was fed at a level of 65% of the diet to groups of 6 lambs each. In addition, the high and low-estrogen meals were fed to stilbestrol-implanted animals.

We are unable to explain at this point why blended material is producing better gains than the high estrogen meal. When a stilbestrol implant is used with low-estrogen meal or high-estrogen meal, gain goes up in proportion to total estrogen content. Note that animals on blended alfalfa meal are doing almost as well as animals on low estrogen meal plus stilbestrol. While these experiments are positive for a growth-promoting response, we cannot at present be certain whether coumestrol or the other forage estrogens are the only active agents in the alfalfas involved.

TABLE 15. 1961 FEEDING TRIAL WITH LAMBS[1]

Group no.	Diet description	Coumestrol	Average daily gain
		p.p.m.	pounds
1	Low-estrogen alfalfa	20	0.292
2	Low-estrogen alfalfa + stilbestrol implant	20	0.486
3	High-estrogen alfalfa + stilbestrol implant	220	0.533
4	High-estrogen alfalfa	220	0.367
5	Blended high and low-estrogen alfalfa	110	0.478

[1] At the end of 6-weeks feeding period. Data from J. E. Oldfield, Oregon State University—personal communication.

Effect of Plant Estrogens on Lactation

Lush, green pasture has long been recognized as having a stimulating effect on milk production. The possibility that plant estrogens are associated with this effect was first suggested by Bartlett and co-workers (1948) at the National Institute for Research in Dairying in Reading, England. They pointed out that a progressive decline in the nonfat solids content of milk occurs during the winter months, followed by a substantial and immediate rise when cows are turned out to pasture in the spring. These workers also pointed out that on "going out to grass," cows often show an increase in milk yield, greater than the amount that can be ascribable to the extra nutrients ingested. These workers assayed samples of forage cut from a number of pastures during the period of active growth and found significant estrogenic activity.

More recently, Bassett and White (1955) of the New Zealand Department of Agriculture attempted to establish a possible correlation between lush pastures, high milk production, and estrogenic activity in the forage. Lactation curves of cows maintained under two different types of grazing management on a typical New Zealand dairy pasture showed that a sharp rise in milk production occurred during

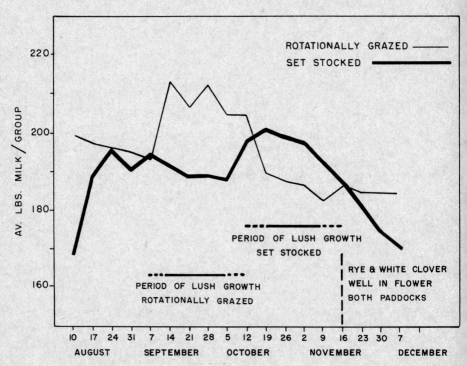

Figure 6. Milk production related to periods of lush pasture growth (Bassett and White, 1955).

the period of lush growth (Figure 6). A large number of samples of the pasture were taken at weekly intervals through the period of lush spring growth and assayed for estrogenic activity. No positive responses were obtained.

This would seem to indicate that there is no correlation between high milk yield and estrogenic content in the pasture. However, in studying the assay procedure for estrogenic activity employed by these workers, I found that their technique, although satisfactory perhaps for the isoflavonoid estrogens, would tend to destroy coumestrol. Therefore, if coumestrol were the dominant estrogen in their white clover, as we have found to be the case with ladino clover, negative assays would result. It would seem to me that this work might bear repeating, taking care to employ an assay procedure that would not destroy coumestrol which might be present in the plant material.

Many workers have used stilbestrol or related compounds to induce udder growth and lactation in dairy animals. A few years ago, workers in the Department of Dairy Husbandry of the Kansas Agricultural Experiment Station (Browning et al., 1957) reported a study to determine the effect on milk production of feeding low levels of stilbestrol to cows. They employed identical twin cows for their study and measured milk response during complete lactations. Each cow treated with stilbestrol produced more 4% FCM (fat corrected milk) than did the controls. Furthermore, treated cows were approximately 6% more efficient in milk production and gained less weight during the test period than did the controls.

It would be very interesting to repeat these experiments with estrogenically potent extracts of forages prepared during the period of lush spring growth. If positive results were obtained with these estrogenic plant extracts, then isolated crystalline plant estrogens should also be evaluated in the same way.

Conclusions

Systematic examination of a much wider group of plants for estrogenic constituents should be fruitful. Considerable more emphasis should be placed on isolating and characterizing estrogenic principles.

It now appears that we may need two separate types of forages. One of these would be a low-estrogen forage for breeding stock, because the naturally occurring estrogens are not desirable here. The second type would be a high-estrogen forage for fattening steers, wethers, and poultry. A possible curtailment of the use of stilbestrol in meat production might provide the stimulus for the development of such a forage.

We cannot at present be certain that estrogens are indeed the growth stimulating factors present in certain forages. Studies of growth stimulation should include concentrates prepared from high-estrogen forages and finally the purified estrogens themselves. Certainly, much more work will have to be done to assess the full potential of coumestrol and other plant estrogens as growth promoters.

Questions and Answers

QUESTION (DR. HISAW, SR.) : I should like, in a way, to ask myself a question by asking you one. Do you share my feeling that it is possible that the animal kingdom might have acquired estrogens from the plant world by one method or another? Estrogenic substances are widely distributed among plants. Since animals evolved in the presence of plants they must have been closely associated with estrogenic substances down through the ages. Such thoughts cause one to wonder if animals acquired estrogens from plants by adaptive means. The first step in this direction might have been the utilization of the estrogenic substances in foods by animals in certain of their metabolic processes, similar to vitamins as we now know them. Also, it seems evident that at present animals are constantly subjected to estrogenic substances from plant sources to which they have become adapted, perhaps dependent, and are unaware.

May I also enquire, while on my feet, if any work has been done on plant estrogens regarding degradation products of the metabolic machinery of the animal body?

ANSWER (DR. BICKOFF) : I certainly agree with you. These materials are certainly very widespread in the plant kingdom and, as you indicate, in invertebrates, where it is hard to describe an actual function for them. Likewise it is difficult to describe a function for them in the plant kingdom. I am sure that as more and more of these plants are studied, it will be found that these estrogens are really very widespread. It has been very surprising to me, and

perhaps it might be to others, that many of the common foods that are eaten every day contain a lot of these estrogens. Whether that is good or bad, I don't know, but they are there. What function do they have? This is the intriguing question, if they do have any function at all. I mentioned, in talking with Dr. Hisaw about this the other day, that my guess is that perhaps these were simply stored products of some sort of metabolism since they do seem to increase as the plant gets older. Dr. Hisaw didn't agree with that; he thought they might more likely serve some function in the plant. This much we don't know. In regard to attempts to find out what types of metabolic products you can obtain, Dr. Booth, who is the pharmacologist in our laboratory, has fed large amounts of coumestrol and has not been able to find any metabolic break-down products. Under the same conditions, he has fed a flavonoid and very easily picked up a number of metabolic products. It seems that there are two possibilities, either the material is being completely fragmented to a point where we don't pick up the phenolic type of break-down products, or it is completely unchanged and simply excreted; we do know that does occur. We are planning to do some work to see how quantitatively we can recover coumestrol from an animal. It may be it simply performs its function and then is excreted. We don't know the whole story on that, but we have not been successful. It does not seem to fragment in the typical way that a flavonoid will.

QUESTION: As Dr. Hisaw has pointed out, we have been with these chemicals for ages. A parallel is the rabbit. You can feed rabbits a stack of pellets, which won't bother them. Is it possible that this material is affecting only humans or the cattle or sheep when it gets in concentration above that which they are used to? Is there any indication that you are getting a change?

ANSWER: Yes, I think that is a point. This is very similar to what happened with sheep in Australia. These sheep had been eating forage for many years containing these estrogens, and quite a bit of them, but it seemed that conditions had to be such that they increased their intake by 25% more than normal, and all of a sudden this very serious reproductive problem developed. Below that level the problem didn't seem to exist at all. It may well be that we have learned to tolerate a small amount there too, and one must get above that critical level (for instance, as I indicated, tulip bulbs were artifically used as food during the war) before one gets into real trouble. We also noted this with mice; one gets a response, say with 0.3 of a milligram of estrogen and a response with 0.2 mg., or a little bit less; then all of a sudden one doesn't get any response. That is, you get a level at which maybe you would expect some response, say at 0.05 of a milligram, and you obtain no response at all. It seems that you have to get past a certain point before you begin to see a response in our work.

QUESTION: We have a certain amount of Scotchbroom on the hill. I am wondering whether or not this might contain sufficient estrogens to be a grazing problem, either with sheep or with goats.

ANSWER: All I can say is that we have assayed Scotchbroom and obtained a noticeable estrogenic response with mice. We might call on Dr. Oldfield to ask what he thought in regard to the problem with sheep.

DR. OLDFIELD: I don't believe there is a serious problem there. I believe that, although there has been some demonstrated estrogenic potency in Scotchbroom, the animals will not eat sufficient amounts of it if there are other materials available for them to eat. Usually this is the case, except in severe over-grazing.

QUESTION: Not even with goats?

DR. OLDFIELD: There again if they have other materials to eat, they will not eat sufficient amounts of it. In severe over-grazing, this could be a problem, I am sure.

REFERENCES

Adler, J. H., and D. Trainin, 1960. A hyperoestrogenic syndrome in cattle. Refuah Veteri-narith, *17*:108-115.

Andrews, F. N., 1958. The estrogenic activity of alfalfa and other forages. Feedstuffs, *30*: (5) :34a-35a, Feb. 1.

Bartlett, S., S. J. Folley, S. J. Rowland, D. H. Curnow, and S. A. Simpson, 1948. Oestrogens in grass and their possible effects on milk secretion. Nature, *162*:845.

Bassett, E. G., and E. P. White, 1955. Oestrogens and New Zealand dairy pastures. New Zealand J. Sci. and Technol., Sec. A, *36*(5) :485-492.

Belak, S., and J. Szathmary, 1937. Die wirkung der wassen bohne auf den oestrus der Mus. I. Biochem. Z., *291*:259-262.

Bennetts, H. W., E. J. Underwood, and F. L. Shier, 1946. A specific breeding problem of sheep on subterranean clover pastures in Western Australia. Australian Vet. J., *22*:2-12.

Bickoff, E. M., A. N. Booth, R. L. Lyman, A. L. Livingston, C. R. Thompson, and F. DeEds, 1957. Coumestrol, a new estrogen isolated from forage crops. Science, *126*:969-970.

Bickoff, E. M., A. N. Booth, R. L. Lyman, A. L. Livingston, C. R. Thompson, and G. O. Kohler, 1958. Isolation of a new estrogen from ladino clover. J. Agr. Food Chem., *6*:536-539.

Bickoff, E. M., R. L. Lyman, A. L. Livingston, and A. N. Booth, 1958. Characterization of coumestrol, a naturally occurring plant estrogen. J. Am. Chem. Soc., *80*:3969-3971.

Bickoff, E. M., A. L. Livingston, A. N. Booth, A. P. Hendrickson, and G. O. Kohler, 1960a. Estrogenic activity in dehydrated and sun-cured forages. J. Animal Sci., *19*:189-197.

Bickoff, E. M., A. N. Booth, A. L. Livingston, and A. P. Hendrickson, 1960b. Observations on the effect of drying on estrogenic activity of alfalfa samples of varying maturity. J. Animal Sci., *19*:745-753.

Bickoff, E. M., A. L. Livingston, A. N. Booth, C. R. Thompson, E. A. Hollowell, and E. G. Beinhart, 1960c. Some variation in estrogenic activity in fresh and dried white clover clones and the ladino variety. J. Animal Sci., *19*:1143-1149.

Biggers, J. D., 1958. "Plant phenols possessing oestrogenic activity." In *The Pharmacology of Plant Phenolics,* J. W. Fairbairn, ed. Academic Press, London, pp. 51-69.

Bounds, D. G., and G. S. Pope, 1960. Light-absorption and chemical properties of miroestrol, the oestrogenic substance of *Pueraria mirifica.* J. Chem. Soc., 3696-3705.

Bradbury, R. B., 1953. Some oestrogenic 4-phenyl-substituted isoflav-3-enes. Australian J. Chem., *6*:447-449.

Bradbury, R. B., and D. E. White, 1951. The chemistry of subterranean clover. Part I. Isolation of formononetin and genistein. J. Chem. Soc., 3447-3449.

Bradbury, R. B., and D. E. White, 1954. Estrogens and related substances in plants. Vitam. and Horm., *12*:207-233.

Browning, C. B., F. C. Fountaine, G. B. Marion, and F. W. Atkeson, 1957. Milk response from feeding diethylstilbestrol to identical-twin cows during complete lactations. J. Dairy Sci., *40*:1590-1598.

Butenandt, A., and H. Jacobi, 1933. Über die darstellung eines krystallisierten pflanzlichen Tokokinins (Thelykinins) und seine identifizierung mit dem a-follikelhormon. Untersuchungen uber das weibliche sexualhormon.10. Z. Physiol. Chem., *218*:104-112.

Butenandt, A., 1940. Zur charakterisierung des oestrogen wirksamen Tokokinins aus Butea superba. Naturwissenschaften, *28*:533.

Carter, M. W., G. Matrone, and W. W. G. Smart, Jr., 1955. Effect of genistin on reproduction of the mouse. J. Nutrition, *55*:639-645.

Cheng, E., C. D. Story, L. C. Payne, L. Yoder, and W. Burroughs, 1953. Detection of estrogenic substances in alfalfa and clover hays fed to fattening lambs. J. Animal Sci., *12*:507-514.

Cheng, E., L. Yoder, C. D. Story, and W. Burroughs, 1954. Estrogenic activity of some iso-flavone derivatives. Science, *120:*575-576.

Cheng, E., and W. Burroughs, 1959. "Estrogenic substances in forages." In *Grasslands,* H. B. Sprague, ed. Amer. Assoc. for the Adv. of Science Pub. 53, pp. 195-202.

Coussens, R., and G. Sierens, 1949. Oestrogenic properties of tulip bulbs. Arch. int Pharma-codyn, *78:*309-312.

El Ridi, M. S., and M. Aboul Wafa, 1947. An oestrogenic substance in palm-pollen grains of the date palm (*Dactylifera palmae* L.) J. Royal Egypt. Med. Assoc., *30:*124-127. Chem. Abs. *42:*5169.

Emmens, C. W., 1941. Precursors of estrogens. J. Endocrinol. *2:*444-458.

Emmens, C. W., R. I. Cox, and L. Martin, 1960. Oestrogen inhibition by steroids and other substances. J. Endocrinol., *20:*198-209.

Engle, P. H., D. S. Bell, and R. R. Davis, 1957. The effect of ladino clover, birdsfoot trefoil, and bluegrass pasture on the rate of conception among ewes. J. Animal Sci., *16:*703-710.

Ershoff, B. H., H. J. Hernandez, and J. H. Matthews, 1956. Beneficial effects of alfalfa on the ovarian development of immature rats fed massive doses of alpha-estradiol. J. Nutri-tion, *59:*147-154.

Fox, C. W., F. F. McKensie, and J. E. Oldfield, 1959. The effects of red clover on reproduc-tion in sheep. J. Animal Sci., *18:*1178 (abstract).

Fox, C. W., J. Kaufmes, R. W. Mason, and J. E. Oldfield, 1957. Effects of feeding red clover (*Trifolium pratense*) on reproduction in laboratory mice. Amer. Soc. Animal Prod. West. Sect. Proc., *8:*Paper 44, 6 pp.

Grisebach, H., 1959. Zur biogenese der isoflavone. Zeitschrift für Naturforschung, *146:*802-809.

Guggolz, J., A. L. Livingston, and E. M. Bickoff, 1961. The detection of daidzein, formono-netin, genistein and biochanin A in forages. J. Agr. Food Chem, *9:*330.

Hale, W. H., P. G. Homeyer, C. C. Culbertson, and W. Burroughs, 1955. Response of lambs fed varied levels of diethylstilbestrol. J. Animal Sci., *14:*909-918.

Hassan, A., and M. Hassan Abou El Wafa, 1947. An oestrogenic substance in pollen-grains of date palm tree, *Phoenix dactylifera* L., Palmae. Nature, *159:*409-410.

Jones, H. E. H., and G. S. Pope, 1960. A study of the action of miroestrol and other oestro-gens on the reproductive tract of the immature female mouse. J. Endocrinol, *20:*229-235.

Kitts, W. D., E. Swierstra, V. C. Brink, and A. J. Wood, 1959. The estrogen-like substances in certain legumes and grasses. I. The quantitative determination of such substances in red clover and oats. Canadian J. Animal Sci., *39:*6-13.

Kitts, W. D., E. Swierstra, V. C. Brink, and A. J. Wood, 1959. The estrogen-like substances in certain legumes and grasses. II. The effect of stage of maturity and frequency of cut-ting on the estrogenic activity of some forages. Canadian J. Animal Sci., *39:*158-163.

Kitts, W. D., 1960. Estrogenic activity of forage crops. Feedstuffs, Jan. 30, *32:* (5) :18.

Loewe, S., 1926. Female sexual hormones from vegetable materials. Germ. pat. 517, 761: through C.A. *25:*2815 (1931).

Lyman, R. L., E. M. Bickoff, A. N. Booth, and A. L. Livingston, 1959. Detection of coumes-trol in leguminous plants. Arch. Biochem. Biophys., *80:*61-67.

Matrone, G., W. W. G. Smart, Jr., M. W. Carter, V. W. Smart, and H. W. Garren, 1956. Effect of genistin on growth and development of the male mouse. J. Nutrition, *59:*235-241.

Matsushima, J., 1959. Dehydrated alfalfa as a protein supplement (with and without stilbes-trol) for fattening cattle. 47th Annual Feeders Day, Nebr. Agri. Exp. Sta., April 17, 1959, pp. 29-32.

Oldfield, J. E., C. W. Fox, and E. M. Bickoff, 1960. Effects of estrogenic activity in alfalfa on growing lambs. J. Animal Sci., *19:*1281 (abstract).

Pedersen-Bjergaard, K., 1933. De l'action folliculinique d'un lipoïde isole des Bacilles tuber-culeux. Compt. rend. soc. biol., *112:*103-105.

Pieterse, P. J. S., and F. N. Andrews, 1956 a. The estrogenic activity of legume, grass, and corn silage. J. Dairy Sci., *39*:81-89.

Pieterse, P. J. S., and F. N. Andrews, 1956 b. The estrogenic activity of alfalfa and other feedstuffs. J. Animal Sci., *15*:25-36.

Pope, G. S., and H. G. Wright, 1954. Oestrogenic isoflavones in red clover and subterranean clover. Chem. and Ind., pp. 1019-1020.

Schoeller, W., M. Dohrn, and W. Hohlweg, 1940. Über eine oestrogene substanz aus der Knolle der siamesischen Schlingpflanze Butea superba. Naturwissenschaften, *28*:532-533 (1940).

Skarzynski, B., 1933a. An oestrogenic substance from plant material. Nature, *131*:766.

Skarzynski, B., 1933b. Estrogenic substances of vegetable origin. Bull. intern. Acad. polonaise, Classe Sci. Math. Nat., *BII*:347-353; through C.A., *28*:4755 (1934).

Solmssen, U. V., 1945. Synthetic estrogens and the relation between their structure and their activity. Chem. Revs., *37*:481-598.

Stob, M., R. L. Davis, and F. N. Andrews, 1957. Strain differences in the estrogenicity of alfalfa. J. Animal Sci. *16*:850.

Story, C. D., W. H. Hale, E. W. Cheng, and W. Burroughs, 1957. The effect of low levels of diethylstilbestrol and plant estrogens upon performance of fattening lambs. Proc. Iowa Acad. Sci., *64*:259-266.

Vatna, S., 1939. Preliminary report on the presence of an oestrogenic substance and a poisonous substance in the storage root of *Butea superba* Roxb. Thai, Sci. Bull. No. 4, 3-9; through C. A., *34*:2929 (1940).

Walter, E. D., 1941. Genistin (an isoflavone glucoside) and its aglucone, genistein, from soybeans, J. Am. Chem. Soc., *63*:3273-3276.

Walz, E., 1931. Isoflavone and saponin glucosides in *Soja hispida. Justus Liebigs Annalen, 489*:118-155.

Wright, P. A., 1960. Infertility in rabbits induced by feeding ladino clover. Proc. Soc. Exp. Biol. Med., *105*:428-430.

Zarrow, M. X., E. A. Lazo-Wasem, and R. L. Shogor, 1953. Estrogenic activity in a commercial animal ration. Science, *118*:650-651.

Zenisek, A., and J. Bednar, 1960. Contribution to the identification of the estrogen activity of hops. American Perfumer, May 1960, pp. 61-62.

Endocrines and the Evolution of Viviparity Among the Vertebrates*

FREDERICK L. HISAW
The Biological Laboratories
Harvard University

THE FIRST of this series of discussions directed attention toward the problem of origin of the endocrine function of the ovarian follicle. The thought was ventured that the earliest function of estrogenic steroids was one concerned primarily with growth of the follicle and vitillogenesis and later, during the evolution of reproductive adaptations, assumed the more general role of hormones regulating the development of morphological structures and behavioral reactions now considered as female secondary sexual characters. Such hormonally controlled characteristics attain their highest degree of specialization in the vertebrates in which the endocrines responsible for follicular growth and ovulation are apparently the same in all species; therefore it is upon this basic background that one must direct his thoughts on the probable evolution of viviparity.

The retention of young during embryonic development in specially adapted structures within or upon the body of the parent is of common occurrence in animals. Most major groups, both invertebrate and vertebrate, have representatives that practice this method of caring for their young. Adaptations for this purpose are of many sorts on the part of both embryo and parent. Such relations may involve only simple harboring of young in broodpouch or marsupium under conditions in which the embryos subsist entirely on their own yolk stores, or they may be nourished by the surrounding parental tissues or take advantage of both possibilities.

The acquirement of a viviparous relationship between parent and developing young in many respects resembles the development of ecological adaptations of animals to a common environment, in that it appears each species solved its problems in its own peculiar way. Therefore, adaptations found in the various viviparous states in nature may hold only a general utilitarian value in common, and cannot be arranged in a progressive evolutionary series. The morphological structures involved may not be homologous and often can be compared only with respect to function. Consequently, a discussion of the evolution of viviparity, except for its most general aspects,

* Aided in part by N.S.F. grant 11213 and U.S.P.H.S. grant A-2673.

119

usually must be confined to development of adaptations that occurred independently in each respective major group. It seems best, in view of these considerations and the chief interests of this colloquium, to discuss aspects of viviparity found in selected representatives of the Vertebrata.

Morphological features of this problem have been presented in several excellent reports (Mathews, 1955, Amoroso, 1959) so I shall emphasize for the most part physiological features and particularly the role that endocrine adaptations might have had in the development of viviparous methods of reproduction leading to those now present in higher mammals.

It has been mentioned in a previous lecture of this series that the endocrines regulating follicular development and ovulation are basically the same in all vertebrates. The hormones directly concerned being the pituitary gonadotropins, FSH and LH and the estrogens, estradiol-17β and estrone, secreted by the ovaries. Therefore, the coordinated interaction of these hormones seems to constitute the principal endocrine mechanism in oviparous, or egglaying, species, which, of course, represents the ancestoral condition from which viviparity in its various forms arose. So, for the general purposes of this discussion, adaptations leading to viviparity can be ordinarily considered as specializations beyond those commonly present in oviparous species. Also, it was at this point that most of the diversity in reproductive processes among vertbrates arose.

Viviparity in some form is present in all classes of vertebrates with the exceptions of cyclostomes and birds. In certain teleost fishes, embryos are retained within the cavity of the ovary until birth. This condition is strikingly different from other vertebrates and nothing really substantial is known about possible endocrine influences. A few urodeles, among the Amphibia, are ovoviviparous and use the oviducts for this purpose. The most advanced condition of viviparity found in anura, if not in Amphibia as a whole, is that described by Lamotte and co-workers (see Gallien, 1959 for references) for an African toad, *Nectophrynoides occidentalis*. About 10 microlecithal ova are retained in a richly vascularized uterine portion of the lower part of the Müllerian ducts where they undergo complete development. The young toads are born after a pregnancy of nine months. The follicle is organized into a corpus luteum which persists throughout gestation, but unfortunately nothing is known about possible endocrine functions.

Among the anamnia, the elasmobranch fishes show conditions of viviparity that in many respects more closely resemble those commonly present in amniotes. Although most are oviparous, quite a few species are ovoviviparous, and some show advanced viviparous conditions. Their chief adaptations are marked specializations of the Müllerian ducts as organs for gestation, the utilization of the foetal yolksac as a yolksac placenta, and development of the corpora lutea in the ovaries.

Although considerable general information has been accumulated regarding reproduction in elasmobranchs, those about which hormonal adaptations are best known are the dogfishes. The European spotted dogfish (*Scyliohinus caniculus*), an oviparous species, has been studied extensively by Dodd and his co-workers (1960), and in our own laboratory we have conducted experiments on two ovoviviparous species, *Squalus acanthias* and *Squalus suckleyi*, and one viviparous species, *Mustelus canis*. The elasmobranchs are geologically very old, having appeared first in the Devonian, and it is a point of interest that in elasmobranchs pituitary-gonadal interactions are well developed. Indeed, observations by Dodd, et al., (1960) on the effects of hypophysectomy in the cyclostome, *Lampetra fluviatalis,* indicate that this adaptation is probably even more ancient and suggests that it could have been a cardinal feature at the very inception of the Vertebrata, perhaps as early as the Ordovician, a span of some 400 million years.

If this be true, it is an exciting thought that the Vertebrata are all fundamentally alike with respect to the hormones involved in follicular development, ovulation, and associated reactions. This implies that all ovipara are hormonally the same and are comparable with reproductive processes in vivipara up until the time of ovulation. Thus, we can state with considerable confidence that in all species the pituitary gland secretes follicle stimulating hormone (FSH), luteinizing hormone (LH), and probably also luteotropic hormone (LtH or prolactin) (Pickford and Atz, 1957; and Pickford, 1959).

As for the steroid hormones of the ovary, one can speak with even more confidence since estradiol-17β, estrone, and progesterone have been isolated and chemically identified in a number of representative species from cyclostomes to mammals as well as in certain invertebrates (see references for first paper of this colloquium). Therefore, a discussion of the evolution of viviparity in the vertebrates can logically begin with consideration of specializations subsequent to ovulation, and the ovipara in large measure can be omitted.

The two dogfish, *Squalus acanthias* and *Mustelus canis,* are suitable examples for a general discussion of adaptations associated with viviparity in elasmobranchs. *Squalus acanthias* (Hisaw and Albert, 1947) is ovoviviparous and has an estimated gestation period of about 22 months. When the large ova enter the uterus they are retained in a common membranous envelope which subsequently deteriorates and the "pups," each with a pendulent yolksac, are set free in the uterine lumen (Figure 1). The ova at ovulation weigh 46-58 grams wet weight, 23-31 grams dry weight, and contain 0.5-0.68 gram of ash. The newborn young weigh 55-86 grams wet weight, 15-25 grams dry weight, and have 0.31-0.53 gram of ash. Therefore, a pup at birth has less solids than a fertilized ovum, indicating that development has been quite independent of contributions of material from the parent. However, during gestation the uterus becomes extremely hyperemic and the endometrium elaborately vascularized; so it seems probable that in addition to supplying oxygen and eliminating metabolic wastes the uterus may also have furnished the embryo with certain substances such as electrolytes, fats, carbohydrates, etc.—even so it appears that this must have been of minor importance.

The conditions of viviparity in *Mustelus canis* are quite different from

	OVUM	CORPUS LUTEUM	WET	DRY	%H₂O	ASH
			WEIGHTS IN GRAMS			
A			46.2 – 58.67	23. – 31.51	50. – 47.6	.500 – .686
B			41.3 – 42.3	19.7 – 22.6	47.6 – 46.8	.420 – .482
Cₐ PUP			11.05	2.25	79.60	.153
YOLK SAC			22.00	12.70	39.00	.275
TOTAL			32.05	14.95	53.38	.428
Cb PUP			25.40	5.80	77.10	.122
YOLK SAC			35.10	20.50	41.50	.331
TOTAL			60.50	26.30	56.50	.453
Cc PUP			25.60	5.45	78.70	.114
YOLK SAC			15.80	7.21	54.30	.122
TOTAL			41.40	12.66	69.40	.236
Cd PUP			13.40	3.42	74.50	.178
YOLK SAC			22.00	12.83	41.70	.214
TOTAL			35.40	16.25	54.10	.392
Cₑ PUP			11.60	2.96	75.50	.160
YOLK SAC			24.30	13.68	43.80	.266
TOTAL			35.90	16.64	53.60	.426
D			55.5 – 84.	15.1 – 25.2	71.8 – 70.	.317 – .530

◄
Figure 1. Comparison of four stages of gestation in the ovoviviparous dogfish, *Squalus acanthias*, as seen at Woods Hole, Massachusetts, in late April and May (stages A and C), and October and November (stages B and D). Stages A and B show extent of growth from early spring to fall of one year and stages C and D show that of similar embryos for a like period the succeeding year. Stages B and C indicate the extent of growth that presumably occurred during the winter. Gestation estimated at approximately 20 to 22 months. (Hisaw and Albert, 1947.)

those described for *S. acanthias*. The gestation period is only about half as long, being approximately 11 months. At ovulation, each ovum is provided with a fluted, membranous capsule and on entering the uterus each is held separately between two folds of the endometrium which extend over the ovum and its envelope laterally and unite by interdigitations on their margins, much after the fashion of a zipper (Figure 2). Thus, each embryo

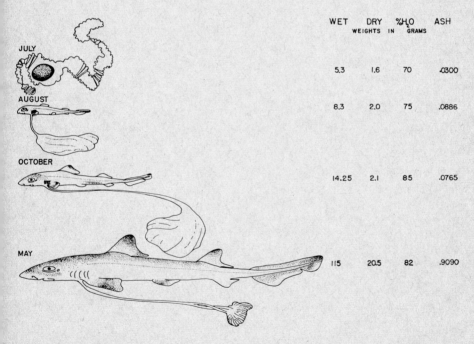

	WET	DRY	%H$_2$O	ASH
		WEIGHTS	IN	GRAMS	
JULY	5.3	1.6	70	.0300
AUGUST	8.3	2.0	75	.0886
OCTOBER	14.25	2.1	85	.0765
MAY	115	20.5	82	.9090

Figure 2. Four stages of development in the viviparous dogfish, *Mustelus canis*, as seen at Woods Hole, Massachusetts. Ovulation occurs about the first of July and parturition in May. Viviparity is shown by small ova, disappearance of yolk, and the formation of a yolk-sac placenta. Normal development occurred in animals hypophysectomized in July and autopsied in October. Gestation approximately 11 months. (Hisaw and Albert, unpublished.)

is isolated from its neighbors and is confined in its own individual compartment.

Also, during the greater part of gestation each embryo is provided with an elaborately fashioned yolksac placenta which is intimately applied to the uterine endometrium, the embryonic and maternal blood vessels being separated mostly by the thickness of their walls and a remnant of the egg-membrane. The ova are much smaller than those of *S. acanthias,* having an average wet weight of only 5.3 grams, 1.6 grams dry weight and 0.030 gram ash. There also is a marked difference between these weights and those of a newborn pup. The average wet weight of pups at term is 115 grams, 20.5 grams dry weight and 0.909 gram ash. Thus, the dependence of the embryos on the parent is obvious.

Although the relation between embryo and parent is very different in these two states of viviparity, there is at present no positive evidence of a corresponding difference in endocrine influences on gestation. The ovaries and ova from pregnant and non-pregnant animals of both species contain large amounts of steroid hormones, especially estrogens. The estrogenic content of ovaries that have large ova previous to ovulation is quite comparable, on a wet-weight basis, with that of most mammalian ovaries; a condition which seems to hold for elasmobranchs in general, both oviparous and viviparous, and which also is a concentration greater than that found in the ovaries of other anamnia that have been investigated. Therefore, yolk in the ova of spiny dogfish at fertilization is well supplied with estrogen which is of course transported with them into the uterus. That such estrogen tends to remain in the yolk for a considerable period during embryonic development is indicated by the observation that some is yet present in the yolksacs of large pups of both *S. acanthias* and *S. suckleyi.*

It is conceivable that in *S. acanthias* and *S. suckleyi* estrogen from the yolksacs of the embryos might contribute to the maintenance of the hyperemic condition of the uterus during gestation. Also, growth of a new generation of ovarian follicles proceeds during pregnancy and they attain almost full size before parturition. Thus, as the estrogen in the yolksacs is depleted there is a corresponding increase in the secretion of estrogen by the ovaries. However, that estrogen from these sources is of importance for gestation is only conjectural. That it may not be essential is indicated by observations on the smooth dogfish *Mustelus canis.* The ova of this viviparous species are small and the yolk is mostly absorbed the first few weeks of pregnancy, and the yolksac is converted into a yolksac placenta which supports the embryo for the greater part of gestation. Also, *M. canis,* unlike *S. acanthias* and *S. suckleyi,* survives well in captivity; consequently it has been possible to subject it to a number of experimental procedures. It has been found, for instance, that the pituitary can be removed at the time of ovulation without apparently interrupting the normal processes of gestation. Eggs that have been ovulated previous to the operation enter the uterus and take up their positions between endometrial folds; the embryos develop, and the yolksac placentas are formed in normal fashion.

Although these observations covered only the first 3½ months of an estimated 11 months period of gestation, and there can be no assurance that pregnancy would have continued until term, there were, at the same time, no indications at the termination of the experiments that it might not have done so. A point of interest in this connection is that following hypophysectomy, involution occurred in all ovarian follicles in which vitellogenesis had been initiated. Therefore it seems probable that in these experiments the uterus was soon deprived of estrogen both from the yolksacs and the ovaries (Hisaw and Abramowitz, 1938, 1939; and Hisaw and Albert, 1947, and unpublished).

Observations of a physiological nature seem to show that the conditions of viviparity described for elasmobranchs may also be similar to those found in certain reptiles. However, reptiles being amniotes have embryos that differ from those of fishes and Amphibia. They are provided with two additional structures, the chorion and allantois, which are of major importance for placental development in the higher vertebrates, and which probably originated as an adaptation among those that arose for living on land and the incubation of embryos under atmospheric conditions within the confines of cleidoic eggs. Although most present day reptiles are oviparous, a number of species, especially among lizards and snakes, have adopted viviparous methods of reproduction. Most reports concerning these reptiles are general descriptions dealing primarily with items of natural history and morphology and comparatively few endocrine studies have been attempted

(Matthews, 1955; and Amoroso, 1959).

Perhaps the most thorough studies, at least for the purpose of the present discussion, were those by Bragdon (1951, 1952, and Bragdon, et al., 1954) on two species of ovoviviparous snakes, *Thamnophis sirtalis* and *Natrix sipedon*. He found that ovariectomy and hypophysectomy of these animals at various stages of pregnancy did not prevent continuation of gestation and normal growth of the embryos, even when the operations were performed soon after ovulation.

The only unusual effects noticed were a greater number of foetal deaths than normal and a disturbance of parturition, shown by retention of young in the uterus or their being born dead. Such, however, might be expected, considering the traumatic effects resulting from the operations and the general metabolic debility of the parent because of pituitary ablation. Also, the possibility that estrogen contained in the yolksacs of the embryos, as mentioned for elasmobranchs, could have partially substituted for loss of the ovaries seemed questionable in snakes, as estrogen is not abundant in the ova (unpublished data for *T. sirtalis*) and the walls of the uterus are thin, suggesting at most a weak estrogen effect. This, and the fact that gestation proceeded, may be taken as rather strong evidence that neither pituitary nor ovarian hormones are essential for uterine development of young in *T. sirtalis* and *N. sipedon*.

This, however, does not signify that the same is true of all live-bearing reptiles. In fact it would appear quite in keeping with evolutionary expectations if instances were found of hormonal interactions in viviparous reptiles similar in some fundamental way to the more specialized conditions in mammals. Weekes (1935), in reviewing placentation among reptiles, considered the chorioallantoic adaptations in certain viviparous lizards (*Chalcides tridactylus, Lygosoma (Liolepisma) entrocasteauxi,* and *L. (L.) weekesae*) as being the most specialized. In these lizards, an elliptical area of the chorion, which has greatly enlarged ectodermal cells and is generously supplied with allantoic blood vessels, is closely applied to a corresponding area of the uterine mucosa which is folded, shows enlargement of the epithelial cells, and is abundantly vascularized. Chorionic cells were not observed to invade the uterine epithelium in these species nor in other viviparous reptiles studied, but there was a marked decrease in the amount of yolk in the ovum at ovulation, as compared with oviparous species and those in which the placenta was less well developed.

Although these observations are inadequate for determining possible endocrine relations they might be considered suggestive. Also, the decrease in amount of yolk in the ovum may be only a reflection of the role assumed by the placenta in fetal nutrition.

A similar occurrence apparently also took place in viviparous elasmobranchs, as indicated by *Mustelus canis.* It seems not unlikely that the chorioallantoic placenta as found in viviparous reptiles could have evolved without endocrine implications and it, like the yolksac placenta of *Mustelus canis,* could develop and perform its nutritive and excretory functions during gestation in the absence of pituitary and ovarian hormones. This seems all the more a possibility considering that *Thamnophis sirtalis* and *Natrix sipedon,* two ovoviviparous snakes, can apparently do this, though normally to a lesser degree. If this be so, it may foretell the gloomy prospect of not being able to discover among extant reptiles instances of adaptive, hormonal interactions that can be accepted as being ancestorial to those in mammals.

However, these thoughts were derived from observations on a few species, which may not be entirely representative. Reptilian endocrinology is yet mostly an unexplored area, so, further investigation may show the situation not to be as it now seems.

Much emphasis has been placed in the past on the relation of corpora lutea of the ovary to viviparity. Modification of the follicular epithelium subsequent to ovulation or associated with follicular atresia is of common occurrence in all classes of the Vertebrata (Brambell, 1956) and the morphology of the structures formed resembles that of mammalian corpora lutea sufficiently to be customarily designated as such. However, this terminology as applied to these structures is misleading insofar as it tends to connote luteal function in a mammalian sense. Although there are valid, morphological homologies, it does not necessarily follow that they function as endocrine glands. In fact, there are certain important differences between corpora lutea of anamnia and at least certain reptiles among the amniota and those of Mammalia.

The histology of the corpora lutea in the lower vertebrates leaves the impression that their principal function is the ingestion and thus elimination of extraneous material remaining in the follicles following ovulation, and the disposal of yolk of moribund eggs during atresia. This process is diagrammatically displayed in both oviparous and viviparous elasmobranchs (Hisaw and Hisaw, 1959) and in reptiles that have been studied (Bragdon, 1952). Such substances as yolk of dead ova, blood cells, tissue fragments, etc. seem to evoke the reaction, as it does not occur in small atretic follicles in which vitellogenesis has not been initiated. Also, their formation is not controlled directly by the pituitary gland, they are invariably seen as the terminal stage of follicular atresia following hypophysectomy. Their function as shown by these observations and others mentioned, is obviously not concerned with viviparity, nor has there been any convincing evidence brought forth proving an endocrine function, in fact, indications so far are quite the contrary.

However, even though a corpus luteum does not possess endocrine function, it does not follow that progesterone is absent. Progesterone is widely distributed in the animal kingdom, being found in the whole ovary and testis as well as in egg yolk and corpora lutea of lower vertebrates (Wotiz, et al., 1958, 1960; Chieffi and Lupo, 1961), and also the ovaries of several species of invertebrates (Botticelli, et al., 1960, 1961). A definite hormonal function for progesterone has not been found in these animals and it seems probable that it may serve only as a precursor for the synthesis of androgens, estrogens, and other steroids in the metabolic series (Dorfman, 1956). If this holds, then it would appear that progesterone took no direct part in the evolution of vivi-

parity in any of the anamnia, and it probably was not of importance in reptiles. However, it is conceivable that progesterone might have acquired endocrine status in the reptilian ancestors of mammals.

One of the most conspicuous hiatuses in the train of tangible knowledge useful in formulating a logical conception of the evolution of viviparity among the vertebrates is the one regarding the transition from reptiles to mammals. The closest approach to the ancestoral condition in mammals is that found in present-day monotremes, which have a number of reptilian characteristics such as yolked ova with membranous shells which are laid and incubated, as well as mammalian traits, the most distinctive being the presence of mammary glands. What is known about endocrine processes in these animals is mostly inferential, having been deduced from those known in the higher mammals. For example, the dependence of mammary function on the pituitary gland, more particularly the secretion of luteotropic hormone (prolactin).

Thus, it seems permissible to assume that the pituitary gland in monotremes secretes luteotropic hormone. Also, the morphology of the corpus luteum appears typically mammalian, although it does show reptilian features such as phagocytosis of yolk during follicular atresia (Garde, 1930). This general appearance of the corpus luteum and its histological and cytological development offer strong evidence for luteal secretion, which in higher mammals is thought to proceed only under the influence of luteotropic hormone (LtH). These same morphological features also seem to indicate a responsiveness to pituitary luteinizing hormone (LH), another mammalian characteristic.

Although our knowledge of the endocrines of reproduction in monotremes is obviously incomplete, the implications mentioned seem sufficiently sound to support the thought that the basic endocrine apparatus in these most primitive species is essentially the same as in other mammals. The principal innovation in the general vertebrate plan, which is found in all mammals, is the formation of a corpus luteum by the action of LH and the secretion of progesterone in response to LtH. These hormones, though present in all vertebrates, had not until this time as far as is known, been brought together in a coordinated system. The problem as to where, when, and how this took place has not been resolved and remains one of the central elements in the nebulous area of thought on the development of mammals from reptilian ancestors.

In a recent discussion (Hisaw, 1959) certain possibilities were considered which might account for the acquisition of secretory function by the corpus luteum. It was mentioned that probably the first step in this direction was the acquirement by the follicle cells of the ability to synthesize small amounts of progesterone. Follicle cells, certainly in all submammalian vertebrates in performance of the menial task of tidying up ruptured follicles following ovulation and phagocytizing yolk of dead ova in atretic follicles became metabolically well acquainted with various sterols and steroids normally found in yolked ova; one of these is cholesterol, a precursor of progesterone. Also, there is evidence

(see first lecture) that the follicle cells in certain species contribute lipoidal material to growing ova.

Although such thoughts may be questioned, it does seem quite evident that secretion of progesterone by the corpus luteum did not become one of its major functions previous to its gaining competence to respond to the action of the pituitary luteotropic hormone (LtH). Also, it is of interest that LtH had already been functioning in other processes associated with reproduction, such as parental behavior, broodiness in birds, secretion of pigeon's milk, etc., in submammalian vertebrates for millions of years before the appearance of mammals as well as that of an estrous cycle with a luteal phase.

Therefore, if it is correct that the formation of progesterone to some extent regularly occurred in the general metabolism of submammalian corpora lutea, then it seems possible that the secretion of progesterone as a major luteal function might have arisen through "capture" and specialization of this process by LtH.

Another consideration which often has been overlooked is that before an adaptation of this sort can be physiologically meaningful there must also be the acquisition of responsiveness of the end organs concerned to the hormone produced. That is, the "capture" of the corpus luteum by LtH and consequent increase of progesterone secretion would appear rather pointless unless at least some degree of responsiveness to progesterone had been acquired by such organs as the uterus. It seems more logical to assume that the train of events was the reverse; that the reproductive organs already had found progesterone, from the gonads, adrenals, or elsewhere, hormonally useful, so, the "capture" of the corpus luteum by LtH was something like the taking over by new management and modernization of an established but antiquated concern.

Specialization of the corpus luteum was associated with other adaptive changes, one of which was the action of the pituitary luteinizing hormone (LH) in the formation of corpora lutea in ruptured follicles following ovulation. Although LH is generally considered essential for ovulation, it does not cause lutenization in ovipara, nor is it required for the formation of corpora lutea as found in ovoviviparous and viviparous elasmobranchs (Hisaw and Abramowitz, 1938, 1939) and reptiles (Bragdon, 1952) that have been studied.

Therefore, it is of special interest that the lutenizing effects of LH seem to be present in monotremes, as it indicates that such effects appeared in egg-laying animals. The fact that certain reptiles retain fully-formed eggs in their reproductive tract until a suitable nesting site is located and lay them all at once has led some investigators to suggest that such activity may be related to luteal function (Matthews, 1955). The relation of corpora lutea to gestation in mammals apparently is the basis for this thought, which is not supported by recent observations that the corpora lutea of submammalian vertebrates do not possess this function. Nevertheless, corpora lutea with such functions may have arisen in reptiles and indeed may yet be found in present-day species. If our opinions are limited to present knowledge, we must concede that corpora lutea in mammals are as distinctive mammalian characters as mammary glands.

Although the exact steps through which the corpus luteum was incorporated as an endocrine gland may remain obscure, there can be little doubt that this adaptation was the most important contributing factor in the evolution of viviparity in mammals. In essence, this involved the addition of a luteal phase in sequence with a preceeding follicular phase which terminated at ovulation; thus the two components of the mammalian estrous cycle were established.

The follicular phase, as previously mentioned, is common to all vertebrates, both ovipara and vivipara, and apparently is regulated by the same pituitary gonadotropins, FSH and LH, and estrogen secreted by developing follicles; whereas, the dominant feature of the luteal phase is the secretion of progesterone by the corpora lutea in response to pituitary luteotropic hormone (LtH). The length of the luteal phase of the estrous cycle corresponds with the functional life of the corpus luteum, which varies in different species. It also is a period during which ovulation does not occur and the uterus assumes a progestational condition. This condition, which is identical with that of early pregnancy, invariably develops during the luteal phase of a cycle regardless of whether or not fertilized ova arrive in the uterus.

This probably was the initial adaptation in the evolution of viviparity in mammals, and it is of interest that it may have appeared first in oviparous species, and, if so, was not associated directly with viviparity. In *Ornithor-*

hynchus, and probably *Echidna,* egg-laying is correlated with the involution of the corpora lutea (Hill and Gatenby, 1926; Garde, 1930). Thus, in monotremes reproduction is accomplished by retaining eggs in the uterus for about a fortnight and incubating them after laying until hatching (Broom, 1895; Asdell, 1946). There is a certain physiological resemblance between this process and the reproductive process in marsupials as shown by the opossum, *Didelphis virginiana,* in that gestation, which is 12-13 days, is also of the same length as the luteal phase of the estrous cycle. Corpora lutea are essential for a successful gestation and parturition coincides with their involution (Hartman, 1923, 1928). The chief difference between this and the situation in monotremes is that instead of egg laying, embryonic development is hastened to an extent that within the relative brief period of 13 days, viable larva-like young are born and are able to find their way into the marsupium. Physiologically, hormonal conditions in both monotremes and marsupials are alike in that the progestational modifications of the uterus depend upon progesterone produced by pituitary-corpus luteum interactions.

One of the notable features in the embryonic development of the opossum, *D. virginiana,* is the relatively large size of the yolksac which almost completely surrounds the embryo. The allantois becomes situated in a depression on the yolksac and does not form contact with the chorion. A similar relation of fetal membranes is apparently the rule in all Didelphia and the yolksac is the most prominent extra-embryonic structure (Marshall, 1922).

It functions as an organ of nutrition which serves in the exchange of materials between parent and fetus, and is commonly referred to as a yolksac placenta. A similar development of the yolksac also occurs in several orders of the Monodelphia, where it may function as an organ of exchange not secondary in importance to the chorio-allantoic placenta with which it is associated (Amoroso, 1959). Although in many instances the yolksac placenta shows marked specialization for fetal nutrition, there is no evidence indicating that it exercises an endocrine influence on gestation.

Prolongation of gestation beyond the normal limit of the luteal phase of the estrous cycle seems to have arisen through specialization of the chorion in the formation of a chorio-allantoic placenta and subsequent adoption of pituitary-ovarian, endocrine functions (Hisaw, 1959). These endocrine adaptations though having certain characteristics in common are quite unlike in others. Specialization of the chorion as an endocrine organ is the reverse of situations we have described previously in which structures attained competence to respond to preexisting hormones. In this case a structure, the chorion, which in its simplest form is a nonglandular membrane designed for an entirely different function, becomes modified into an organ which secretes active agents which may be chemically identical with or differ from hormones normally produced by the ovaries and pituitary, and which, physiologically, can substitute for or mimic, in a special way, their endocrine actions. Thus, the chorion in many species of mammals has adopted certain pituitary and ovarian hormonal functions.

It is not surprising, and in fact seems logical, that an endocrine gland which secretes a hormone for a particular set of functions may extend its realm of influence during evolutionary development by assuming hormonal control of other tissues and organs that acquire ability to respond to its action. It apparently was in some such way that the pituitary gonadotropins, FSH and LH, and luteotropin, LtH, became associated with the ovarian hormones, estrogens, and progesterone, in the organization of the mammalian estrous cycle (Hisaw, 1959). However, requirements for the endocrine specialization of the chorion were considerably different. Its problem was to evoke responses in organs of the female reproductive tract which were already integrated in an established and functioning hormonal system. Therefore, it seems a reasonable expectation that its specialization should involve the elaboration of steroids such as estrogens and progesterone and proteinaceous substances resembling pituitary gonadotropins. The surprising thing is that in certain instances it succeeded in accomplishing both.

The length of gestation in mammals above marsupials exceeds that of the luteal phase of their respective estrous cycles. This lengthening of gestation is accomplished either by prolonging the functional life of the corpus luteum or by the adoption of complete endocrine control of pregnancy by the placenta or a combination of both.

The evolutionary sequence of the adaptations involved is far from clear, and our judgment regarding probable developments must be based on a relatively few species whose physiology of reproduction is well enough known to

be useful for comparisons. Also, our knowledge of these matters, as they may apply to mammals as a whole, is such that the most that can be accomplished at present is to call attention to certain differences and probable trends that may have been taken in the endocrine specialization of the placenta, and hopefully postpone for the future the consideration of possible steps in their evolutionary progression.

A comparison of the general endocrine situation, as it pertains to the placenta, has been presented (Hisaw, 1959) for several species that have been studied more thoroughly than others. Therefore, only certain of the more salient features will be used for present purposes. Animals about which most is known are laboratory rodents, particularly rats and mice, the monkey (*Macaca mulatta*), the human being, and the mare. Comparisons which include so few species are obviously not adequate for the determination of stages in evolution, but they do show wide variations and thus indicate the remarkable range in adaptability of the placenta as an endocrine organ.

It would seem, from studies of the rat and mouse, that one of the earliest, if not the first, endocrine functions of the placenta was the secretion of luteotropin. The estrous cycle of a rat (4 to 5 days) is automatically prolonged into a pseudopregnant period of 12 to 14 days. The endocrines regulating pseudopregnancy are the same as those of the luteal phase of an estrous cycle, that is, luteal function is maintained by the pituitary luteotropic hormone (LtH). Also, gestation depends upon the presence of functional corpora lutea; abortion invariably occurs following castration during the first half of pregnancy and usually results after removal of the ovaries a week or ten days before term (Zeiner, 1943). However, hypophysectomy on the eleventh or twelfth day or later does not interrupt gestation, whereas, pituitary ablation at an earlier time does without exception (Pencharz and Long, 1933; Selye, Collip, and Thomson, 1933).

It also is significant that the time at which hypophysectomy does not interrupt pregnancy coincides with that at which mesoderm and allantoic blood vessels grow into the ectodermal trophoblast of the developing placenta (Huggett and Pritchard, 1945). These observations and those of Astwood and Greep (1938) that the placenta contains a luteotropic substance, and those of Ray, et al. (1955) that placental implants prevent abortion following hypophysectomy on the sixth day of pregnancy, offer convincing evidence that the corpora lutea are under the influence of a placental luteotropic hormone for approximately the last half of a normal gestation. Similar evidence for the presence of a placental luteotropin also can be offered for the mouse (Gardner and Allen, 1942).

Discussions of gestation, particularly in mammals, usually place the chief emphasis on luteal function and the role of progesterone, with little or no consideration of the possible importance of estrogens. The fact that estrogens, though often in small amounts, are always present during pregnancy may be of considerable significance. In mammals such as the rat, mouse, and rabbit, and certain other species, it is known that follicular development is not completely suppressed during pregnancy, so it seems that estrogen is probably secreted by the ovary. The placental luteotropin of rats, however, does not stimulate follicular growth, although it does produce mammary development, and in these respects resembles pituitary LtH (Ray, et al., 1955).

Gardner and Allen (1942) found that in mice hypophysectomy on the tenth day of pregnancy caused involution of the ovarian follicles, whereas luteal function and gestation continued. This casts doubt on the importance of follicular activity, and indeed indicates that estrogen from the ovary is not essential for gestation in these animals. However, the placenta has been suggested as a possible source of estrogen, and although this has not been satisfactorily resolved for rats and mice, it is well known that steroid secretion is a major function of the placenta in animals such as the horse, monkey, and human being.

Although secretion of a luteotropin may have been the earliest specialization of the chorion, it has been found that in certain of the higher mammals, such as the Equidae and Primata, the placenta also has adopted ovarian function and is a source for the production of estrogen and progesterone. Recent attention has been called to this by Hisaw (1959) and Zarrow (1961), and also the fact that such adaptations have provided autonomous endocrine functions for the chorio-allantoic placenta in such species. For instance, it has been shown in the Rhesus monkey (*Macaca mulatta*) that after the placenta is established gestation can proceed in the absence of the ovaries, fetus, and pituitary. So far, all three of these operations have not been performed simultaneously on the same animal, but it appears possible that under such circumstances the placenta would continue its normal endocrine functions until the usual time of parturition. So, the chorion, which originally was designed for the needs of an embryo in the cleidoic environment of a shelled egg, assumed endocrine adaptations that enabled it to live an independent existence in the Müllerian duct.

This physiological modification of the chorion raises certain thoughts that seem worthy of consideration with respect to the evolution of viviparity among the vertebrates. The first of these is the fact that the Müllerian ducts were utilized successfully for viviparous purposes in animals like elasmobranchs before the advent of such foetal membranes as the amnion and chorion. Also, it seems from available evidence that ovarian progesterone, though present, does not function as a progestational hormone in such animals, whereas estrogens, which are known to exercise hormonal influences on structures originating from the Müllerian ducts, appear to be the principal ovarian hormones in viviparous anamnia.

Estrogens appear to exercise hormonal functions in the reproductive tracts of all vivipara in which the Müllerian ducts are used, whereas, progesterone has not been convincingly demonstrated as having a progestational role in animals other than mammals. A corpus luteum as a functional source of progesterone during gestation probably arose in the reptilian ancestors of mammals. Although it yet may be proven to have hormonal function in some extant viviparous species, available evidence is at best circumstantial.

Furthermore, it seems quite significant that tissues other than those of the reproductive tract have not only acquired responsiveness to gonadal hormones but also have become adapted for the facilitation of viviparity. At the same time embryos of many species, both vertebrate and invertebrate, have shown abilities to form adaptive devices for viviparous existence in various regions of the parental body. In fact, it appears that the mechanisms of viviparity are methods mostly for establishing an embryo in a particular locality rather than maintaining it over a prolonged gestation period. This is brought about in various ways, both hormonal and otherwise or a combination of factors, depending upon the adaptations of the species. Therefore, when viviparity among the vertebrates is viewed critically as a whole, the general impression gained is that the adaptations involved do not constitute a progressive phylogenetic series of events, but rather, a remarkable variety of ways by which a group of related organisms have solved a common problem.

Questions and Answers

QUESTION: I want to ask you about perhaps another Phylum, the Echinodermata, which has at least a pseudo-viviparity. Does anybody know anything about the structures there? Is there any similarity at all?

ANSWER: No, there need not be a similarity, and if there is, it is probably incidental. There seems to have been no set plan in the development of viviparity. The care and nourishment of young, of course, are implied in all conditions and degrees of viviparity. Otherwise, it seems nothing could be more diverse than the structures utilized for this purpose and comparisons that seem to possess some physiological validity with respect to comparative endocrinology can be made only between closely related groups, such as the different classes of vertebrates.

REPLY: And no one knows of any similarity of glands, or anything?

DR. HISAW: There are, of course, certain glandular similarities in distantly related species, but their biological meanings usually are not known. Endocrinology in the invertebrates is something that needs much more attention than it has received.

QUESTION: I wonder if there is any information on the viviperous tsetse? They are not Dr. Strand's louse, by any chance, are they?

ANSWER: Viviparity of various sorts is common among insects. This means, of course, that different kinds of relations between parent and young are found. However, little is known about the physiology of such relations.

REPLY: There is supposed to be a secretion produced that larvae feed on, too, like pigeon's milk.

DR. HISAW: No doubt something of this nature can be found in different groups of animals. The best example of a relationship of this kind is found in scorpions. There seem to be about as many morphological adaptations for this purpose as one finds among insect larvae that have taken on an aquatic existence.

QUESTION: How are they going to live in the water?

ANSWER: I was referring of course to larval adaptations of aquatic insects. The larvae of such insects, as you know, may go through almost all of their development in an aquatic environment. Some come to the surface for air, some dive and take air with them, some remain submerged, and many kinds of extensions of the body surface are used as gills. The general requirements of an organ of respiration seems to be all that is common to some of these structures.

REPLY: But it certainly is evident there is no relationship between that found in animals, like the insects, and the vertebrate cycle.

DR. HISAW: Perhaps it is safer to say that less is known about insects with respect to this than is known about vertebrates. We do know that endocrine systems are present in insects, and they operate by interactions and feed-back systems very much as those found in vertebrates. The basic physiological principles involved in both instances are probably very much the same, although the biochemical substances and the organs from which they are derived are not homologous nor the functions identical. I feel that our knowledge of endocrinology in insects is too limited at present to attempt more than very generalized comparisons with vertebrates.

QUESTION: I am curious about these nonfunctional corpora lutea, as you call them, curious about whether they are really nonfunctional. Do they have any physiological characteristics that would cause us to suspect any kind of glandular or secretory activity? I am not familiar with them.

ANSWER: I am sorry if the term "nonfunctional" as applied to a kind of luteal body gave the impression of no function at all. What was implied is a lack of ability to secrete progesterone, and they are "nonfunctional" in the sense that they do not take part in maintaining a viviparous condition. They originate, of course, from follicle cells and are represented in vertebrates by the granulosa. Therefore, they originally have all the functions of follicle cells during follicular development, vitellogenesis, etc., which were mentioned briefly in this and my previous lecture.

The follicular epithelium in submammalian vertebrates and apparently in certain invertebrates becomes modified into "luteal" bodies or corpora lutea following ovulation or follicular atresia. The first stage in such development involves a phagocytic reaction of the follicle cells to debris that may remain in the ruptured follicle or the yolk of a moribund ovum in the case of atresia. Although indications of a similar reaction have been described for certain mammals, these structures differ from mammalian corpora lutea in that apparently they do not secrete progesterone, they can be removed without disturbing gestation, and they can develop in hypophysectomized animals, indicating LH is not required for their formation.

REPLY: Are they just phagocytes?

DR. HISAW: Phagocytosis is the most conspicuous activity observed.

QUESTION: I am still worried about the matter of progesterone. Your argument is that it is a very old material. It starts a way back, and yet you emphasize the point that it came into its own only in the higher mammals. Now, do you feel it has other functions in addition to those dealing with viviparity, and would you comment on this further?

ANSWER: We obviously do not know all the functions progesterone has in animals, but some functions we feel quite sure it does have must be very old — indeed, much older than its hormonal function in viviparous mammals. If our reasoning is correct, progesterone is one of the steroids formed as a precursor in the synthesis of androgens and estrogens from cholesterol and probably related sterols. It also appears that androgens and estrogens arose before they were utilized as hormones in the development of recognized secondary sexual characteristics. It was suggested that the original function of estrogen was probably concerned with follicular development, vitellogenesis, etc. These processes must indeed be very old.

The fact that progesterone is present in both invertebrates and vertebrates, male and female, castrated and normal not only indicates a general distribution but also raises questions as to functions not related directly to reproduction. It is thought to be a precursor of the adrenal cortical steroids, and of course it may have many other functions yet unknown. However, in the area of reproduction progesterone is generally thought of as being secreted by the corpus luteum. Although it seems reasonable to think that progesterone to some extent must be formed in the metabolic processes of all follicles, this does not necessarily indicate that it has a hormonal function. The point emphasized was the apparent absence of convincing evidence that the corpus luteum in animals below mammals had a role in viviparity. Does this answer what you have in mind?

REPLY: Yes, in part. It seems to me that in the birds it is true, is it not, that there are a number of synergistic actions between progesterone and other factors, and it seems to me that perhaps in the lower vertebrates this material produced in the course of production of other materials may have some synergistic effects, and I wonder if there is anything known about the physiology there?

DR. HISAW: I do not recall, at present, a valid incidence of this among the invertebrates but synergistic effects between estrogen and progesterone in the vertebrates, particularly mammals, have been a common observation.

REPLY: So that it might have come into the picture in a modest sort of a way?

DR. HISAW: In my opinion, this is probably correct. For instance, we have reason for thinking that both estrogen and progesterone are present simultaneously in the follicular apparatus. Furthermore, one should think that estrogen would be the dominant secretion during follicular development and would tend to wane as the process neared completion. If so, one might expect a tendency for progesterone to accumulate as the synthesis of estrogen decreased, thus changing the balance between the two steroids. That some such change in estrogen-progesterone relationship might take a responsible part in the process of ovulation is a thought that has been in mind for some time. This is supported by the observations of several workers who report the induction of experimental ovulation, *in vivo* and *in vitro*, in several species by the addition of progesterone—but not estrogen. It also is true, of course, that ovulation was universally practiced by animals for a very long time before the appearance of pituitary-ovarian interactions. So, it could be that ovulation in its simplest form is due to local steroid action, and collateral influences, such as those from the pituitary, functioning largely as accessory information channels and timing devices. Such thoughts, we must admit, are conjectural if not fanciful and we can only hope that they are not too farfetched for the purposes of our colloquium.

REFERENCES

Amoroso, E. C., 1959. "Comparative anatomy of the placenta." In *The Uterus.* Ann. N.Y. Acad. Sci. *75:*855-872 (article 2).

Asdell, S. A., 1946. *Patterns of Mammalian Reproduction.* New York, Comstock Publ. Co.

Astwood, E. B., and R. O. Greep, 1938. A corpus luteum-stimulating substance in the rat placenta. Proc. Soc. Exp. Biol. and Med., *38:*713-716.

Botticelli, C. R., F. L. Hisaw, Jr., and H. H. Wotiz, 1960. Estradiol-17β and progesterone in ovaries of starfish (*Pisaster ochraceous*). Proc. Soc. Exp. Biol. and Med., *103:*875-877.

Botticelli, C. R., F. L. Hisaw, Jr., and H. H. Wotiz, 1961. Estrogens and progesterone in the sea urchin and pecten. Proc. Soc. Exp. Biol. and Med., *106:*887-889.

Bragdon, D. E., 1951. The nonessentiality of the corpora lutea for the maintenance of gestation in certain live-bearing snakes. J. Exper. Zool., *118:*419-435.

Bragdon, D. E., E. A. Lazo-Wasem, M. X. Zarrow, and F. L. Hisaw, 1954. Progesterone-like activity in the plasma of ovoviviparous snakes. Proc. Soc. Exp. Biol. and Med., *86:*477-480.

Bragdon, D. E., 1952. Corpus luteum formation and follicular atresia in the common garter snake, *Thamnophis sirtalis.* J. Morphol., *91:*413-445.

Brambell, F. W. R., 1956. "Ovarian changes." In Marshall's *Physiology of Reproduction,* 3rd ed., Vol. I, Pt. I, pp. 387-542. London, Longmans, Green and Co.

Broom, R., 1895. Note on the gestation in *Echidna.* Proc. Linn. Soc. N.S.W., *10:*576-577.

Chieffi, G., and E. Lupo, 1961. Identification of oestradiol-17β, testosterone and its precursors from *Scylliorhinus stellaris* testes. Nature, *190:*169-170.

Dodd, J. M., P. J. Evennett, and C. K. Goddard, 1960. Reproductive endocrinology in cyclostomes and elasmobranchs. Symp. Zool. Soc. London, No. 1, pp. 77-103.

Dorfman, R. I., 1956. Metabolism of androgens, estrogens, and corticoids. Am. J. Med., *21:*679-687.

Gallien, L., 1959. "Endocrine basis for reproductive adaptations in Amphibia." In *Comparative Endocrinology.* A. Gorbman, ed. New York, Wiley, pp. 479-487.

Garde, M. L., 1930. The ovary of *Ornithorhynchus* with special reference to follicular atresia. J. Anat., London, *64:*422-453.

Gardner, W. U., and E. Allen, 1942. Effects of hypophysectomy at midpregnancy in the mouse. Anat. Rec., *83:*75-97.

Hartman, C. G., 1923. The oestrous cycle in the opossum. Am. J. Anat., *32:*353-421.

Hartman, C. G., 1928. The breeding season of the opossum (*Didelphis virginiana*) and the rate of intrauterine and postnatal development. J. Morphol., *46:*143-215.

Hill, J. P., and J. B. Gatenby, 1926. The corpus luteum of the monotremata. Proc. Zool. Soc. London, *47:*715-763.

Hisaw, F. L., 1959. "Endocrine adaptations of the mammalian estrous cycle and gestation." In *Comparative Endocrinology,* A. Gorbman, ed., pp. 533-552.

Hisaw, F. L., and A. A. Abramowitz, 1938. The physiology of reproduction in the dogfish, *Mustelus canis.* Report of the Woods Hole Oceanog. Inst., 1937, pp. 21-22.

Hisaw, F. L., and A. A. Abramowitz, 1939. Physiology of reproduction in the dogfish, *Mustelus canis* and *Squalus acanthias.* Report of the Woods Hole Oceanog. Inst., 1938, p. 22.

Hisaw, F. L., and A. Albert, 1947. Observations on the reproduction of the spiny dogfish, *Squalus acanthias.* Biol. Bull., *92:*187-199.

Huggett, A. St. G., and J. J. Pritchard, 1945. Experimental foetal death: the surviving placenta. Proc. Roy. Soc. Med., *38:*261-266.

Marshall, F. H. A., 1922. *The Physiology of Reproduction,* Chapter X. New York, Longmans, Green and Co.

Mathews, L. H., 1955. The evolution of viviparity in vertebrates. Memoirs of the Soc. for Endocrinology, No. 4, pp. 129-148.

Pencharz, R. I., and J. A. Long, 1933. Hypophysectomy in the pregnant rat. Am. J. Anat., *53:* 117-139.

Pickford, G. E., 1959. "The nature and physiology of the pituitary hormones of fishes." In *Comparative Endocrinology,* A. Gorbman, ed. New York, Wiley, pp. 404-420.

Pickford, G. E., and J. W. Atz, 1957. *The Physiology of the Pituitary Gland of Fishes.* New York, New York Zoological Society.

Ray, E. W., S. C. Averill, W. R. Lyons, and R. E. Johnson, 1955. Rat placenta hormonal activities corresponding to those of pituitary mammotropin. Endocrinology, *56:*359-373.

Selye, H., J. B. Collip, and D. L. Thomson, 1933. Anterior pituitary and lactation. Proc. Soc. Exp. Biol. and Med., *30:*588-589.

Weekes, H. C., 1935. A review of placentation among reptiles with particular regard to the function and evolution of the placenta. Proc. Zool. Soc. London, pp. 625-646.

Wotiz, H. H., C. R. Botticelli, F. L. Hisaw, Jr., and I. Ringler, 1958. Identification of estradiol-17β from dogfish ova (*Squalus suckleyi*). J. Bio. Chem., *231*(No. 2) :589-592.

Wotiz, H. H., C. R. Botticelli, F. L. Hisaw, Jr., and A. G. Olsen, 1960. Estradiol-17β, estrone, and progesterone in the ovaries of dogfish (*Squalus suckleyi*). Proc. Natl. Acad. Sci., *46*(No. 4) :580-583.

Zarrow, M. X., 1961. "Gestation." In *Sex and Internal Secretions,* 3rd ed., Vol. II, pp. 958-1031.

Zeiner, F. N., 1943. Studies on the maintenance of pregnancy in the white rat. Endocrinology, *33:*239-249.

Materials and Species Covered

Materials